UMBULALA

THROUGH THE EYES OF A LEOPARD

LENA GODSALL BOTTRIELL

Artwork: Paul Bottriell
Photoprints: Paul Bottriell & Lena Godsall Bottriell

Questech Productions

 First published in Great Britain 1993 by

Questech Productions Limited

P. O. Box 141, Aylesbury, BUCKS, HP17 0YD, UK.

A CIP catalogue record for this book is available from the British Library

ISBN 0 9521871 0 8

Printed and bound in Great Britain by BPCC Hazells Ltd., Aylesbury.

Also by Lena Godsall Bottriell

King Cheetah: The Story of the Quest

Published by E.J. Brill of Leiden

TO PAUL

*Whose tale this is.... born
of his tapestry of
campfire anecdotes,
woven down the silk of
African nights*

INTRODUCTION

Umbulala is no fairytale. Rather it is a fantasy of the truest kind - a plain tale out of Africa of the day-to-day existence of a big cat born to hunt; a magnificent predator sculptured in the classic mould which, along with its breed, is one of the most ferocious of all wild animals.

Leopards inhabit very nearly the entire expanse of Africa and Asia, through every conceivable terrain and climactic zone, from near-desert to snowcapped mountain peak. They are the most adaptable of the cats; and while still eagerly sought after for their hide, they are also a resilient species. Big game hunters, poachers and field zoologists alike consider leopard the most dangerous of animals: pound for pound, the jungle's most consistently successful hunter-killer. Cornered or surprised, it fears nothing. Many is the tale of encounters with leopard as dreaded as any confrontation with lion, elephant, rhino or buffalo. Among native peoples it is the most feared of the cats for its courage and tenacity, its ferocity, its cunning patience.

The leopard is also one of the most beautiful of the wild's animals, capable of quite matchless tenderness as a mother. Nature's paradox. Here lies one of the great contradictions of nature, so often noted in gloriously coloured birds with voices of tuneless rasp; or in the deceptive loveliness of plants that disguise a poisonous intent. Many is the beast whose beauty belies its nature. No better does this apply than to the big cats of jungle and savanna; no better than to the leopard. Yet, as physically perfect, aesthetically pleasing creatures that they are, they can never be amiable pussycats chastened to be at humankind's beck and call. The individuality

of each within the whole is inviolate. Nature's design for them is not to win approval, only respect.

Umbulala is a panther - a term popularly applied to black leopards in Africa - born of the loins of a spotted leopard. It is not a story where the ferocity of the cat has been glossed over in a misplaced, anthropomorphic way; nor the dangers that lurk in what, in the minds of some, is a wondrous paradise for animals of all kinds. The bush, the jungle, is the most neutral of places, filled with warmth and beauty, abounding in food and water for those with the care and wit to find both. It is also unforgiving, where all must walk a narrow path because with just one careless step, injury or death awaits - perilous pitfalls to which predators are as susceptible as the animals upon which they prey.

Woven through the story like a silver thread is the female leopard's struggle to raise her young - through cubhood, thence adolescence and on into early adulthood when each must break away to establish territories and lives of their own; a tale that forgets neither the small things of the jungle, nor its humour. Umbulala develops from fumbling cubhood - where everything and anything is prey to be attacked - into a master hunter feared by all. Umbulala is a leopard of such proportions as to compare favourably in size with an 18 month old lioness, gifted by nature with a sharp mind and instinct, and aided by incomparable senses that are the hallmark of the leopard: carnivore consummate, perfect distillation of the predator supreme. In essence, a cat like no other - the stuff of legend.

CONTENTS

	Page
LEOPARD's DEN	1
EARLY DAYS	14
FISH AND FOWL	30
JUNGLE LORE	44
SEASON's SHADOW	58
NOSE TO THE WIND	77
THE PRECIPICE	93
BOTH SIDES OF THE LEAF	108
THE BULLFROG's DILEMMA	117
WHY	137
THE WINDING WAYS	155
WHAT THE SWALLOW SAYS	172
CROWN OF HORNS	188
BEYOND THE CIRCLE	197
REFERENCES: BLACK LEOPARD IN AFRICA	210
LIST OF ILLUSTRATIONS	211
GLOSSARY	212

All life's cycle is the
gathering herds,
inscribing nature's
whim across the land

LEOPARD's DEN

Trees and bushes of varying mien swayed with every whimper of the night wind. Gently, on each wisp of breeze, watery sprays of dew sprinkled the ground from spider webs that wreathed the jungle's shadowy congregations of green like glistening rosaries. Only those sounds of jungle life that rise to greet the moon wracked the dark remembered night, muffled here and there by rain cloud that had been sombrely announcing itself since dusk. A leopard coughed in the dusky shadows - a sonorous rasp of warning known to all who wander the jungle's spreading traces, its forbidding tremolo declaiming a meaning few could misread.

Struggling wearily through the damp undergrowth, her sturdy padded paws squelching, sometimes slipping in their muddy tread, Ingwe humped the fresh carcass of a young bushpig back to her den. With its neck gripped firmly in her jaws, the pig's lank body trailed heavily between the leopardess's powerful forelegs. Her ermine chest heaved wearily - the soft, shy quality of the fur somewhat decrying the stereotyped image of roughing it wild. She was tired, so very nearly sapped of energy; but with that unerring determination of her breed she urged herself to go on, breathing out a silent supplication to some higher order.

1

A jackal bayed at the pale moon, as somewhere on the night a carillon of zebra bells pealed out in the crisp air. Tongues of wind licking through the dank foliage played about the big cat's face, stinging her nose and eyes in chill indifference. Long grassy tresses caught and hindered her; sinewy tentacles of vine, with tiny unseen claws, clung to her legs and flanks; while, as if in league, even the carcass she was dragging appeared bent on tripping her up and checking her course! Ingwe was heavy with young, hence her difficulty. Yet she'd had no choice but to hunt this night. It was her last chance to make a kill before the birth; a birth all her instincts were telling her was not far off. That she would be needing all her strength for then was a truth she wasn't likely to forget.

Her chosen lair for the occasion was a cave high up on a craggy escarpment - a cosy indentation hollowed out among a welter of sturdy granite boulders, and crowded from sight by an unruly scramble of trees and shrubs jumbled together in profuse abandon. The ground beneath sloped away sharply, its cover of frothy ferns dancing attendance on a tangle of vengeful *wait-a-bit* scrub with mean, hooked, clutching thorns that will prick and stick fast to an animal's skin, or fur, the more it pulls away.

Breathing hard from the climb up the escarpment, just inside the narrow opening to the cave Ingwe dropped the carcass atop a pile of stark bones, picked clean from previous feasts. She sighed with the relief of one who has just shed a heavy load and for a moment, her nostrils flared wide, remained where she stood, gasping in salutary draughts of fresh air. The breeze off the edge of the escarpment cooled and revived her, bringing with it the welcome rain that soothed the toil of night away.

Presently, more composed, she vigorously shook herself dry, then turned her attention to the task of lodging the carcass of the bushpig further in from the cave entrance, and safe out of the way of marauders. This done, she checked her surroundings, slowly casting a careful eye around the den, before ambling languidly over to a quiet back corner well away from the damp of the entrance. Gone was the nonchalant, slouching gait distinctive of leopard. In its place was a laboured trundle. She was still panting heavily as she sank down gratefully onto the warm granite floor of the cave.

Sleep beckoned seductively, caressing her brow. First, however, she would attend to a chore characteristic of cats, male and female, the jungle over - an elaborate dedication to grooming that sets the leopard apart. Usually lustrous in its markings of black-brown spots - circled together in broken rings suggestive of rosettes, and emblazoned across a hide amber and smooth as wild honey - her coat was now scuffed and smeared with the spoils of the hunt. Yet tired out as she was, Ingwe set about cleaning herself with prodigious concern.

Despite the dampness of the greenery she'd brushed against on the journey back, and then lastly the rain that had caught her on the escarpment, blood on her face and chest, shoulders and paws still clung obtrusively. The coarse tongue worked briskly: first over chest and shoulders, then around claws of ductile precision, each in its way a stiletto-tipped sabre of lethal propensity. Ingwe, licking each forepaw in turn, before rubbing the damp fur against her blood-smeared face, couldn't help thinking how privileged she was in Mother nature favouring her with such formidable weapons. Some time passed in this way, the leopardess swinging dreamily between task and meditation. Eventually, heavy with the need to sleep, her head nodded.

Presently she began to doze, fitfully at first; falling into a deeper repose as slumber's trail led her onward to dawn. With its approach, faint ebbs of light began to shyly probe the blue indigo of daybreak, building, moment by moment, into limpid, silvery shafts that filtered in through every chink and cranny of rock, gently coaxing awake those that slept. Ingwe stirred, purring softly as the first warm rays of light began to bath away the damp of night from the rock around her. She loved the time around sunrise, bringing as it did an abiding sense of rebirth to everything it touched.

Ingwe stretched lazily into the rays. A sudden, jagged pain struck her sharply in the pit of the stomach, stinging her into consciousness. The birth of her little ones was fast approaching. Catching her unawares, the big cat gasped, her belly, taut and distended with cub, billowing in and out with every fresh stab of pain as if she had just run a great chase. The pains continued to come and go, and she seemed set for a restless day spent napping uneasily between further like messages from Mother nature, and tearing casually at the kill she'd expended so much energy on the night before. Ingwe's thoughts strayed to her mate Bulala, and she sniffed petulantly:

"He's never around when he's needed!"

Pricking her ears up, she regarded the bushpig's profile with a quizzical air,

"And if he was, he'd probably be filling his stomach on my kill!"

she huffed in afterthought. She fell to licking her thick, ochry coat, sumptuous in its melding of pattern and colour. With such precise originality of design, the leopard's spots are arranged in shapes akin to the very pug-marks left by the cat's paws. Amid the shadowed, mottled vegetation that the leopard invariably gravitates to, such markings make for a camouflage that leaves the leopard virtually undetectable. And as she thoughtfully licked her coat, Ingwe, with the quiet self-assurance of the winner, mused on the wisdom of such things.

There came a welcome cessation in the pain, and Ingwe relaxed a little. She was yawning widely, in the process of rolling onto her side when a faint, barely perceptible sound, of what might be an intruder, brought her reeling to attention. Like a trigger sprung at the ready, Ingwe flipped back onto her stomach. Almost immediately the big leopardess crouched, her hairline senses alert to the slightest nuance of a presence, every sinew, every nerve stretched poised for attack!

Suddenly she checked herself. It might be more prudent, given her condition, to warn her visitor off, and thus save herself the strain of a fight she might not be up to. In the face of a big male hyaena her extreme state of expectation would be a definite disadvantage! True to say that if one condition in particular applied to Ingwe - if she in fact were a he - then it would be a different matter. And all at once, Ingwe knew just what do. Mustering all her reserves of vocal prowess, she let forth such an explosive roar of attack in as basso profundo timbre as she could summon up, even her fur stood on end!

A gruff cough floated back over the echoing fury - but it bore no malice. Indeed, it sounded almost surprised. Ingwe was still pondering this when, in the beat of a moth's wing, Bulala's massive form squeezed through the narrow entrance to the den - and came straight toward her, the bushpig not even getting a second glance! Ingwe was so ashamed of herself, a dark guilt at once gripped her, like a mantis does its prey. Such prejudgement never did any cat any good, she well knew. But Bulala was blissfully unaware of any such pangs of remorse Ingwe might be suffering on his behalf, and promptly proceeded to lick away the traces of blood still smearing her face.

"You look tired Ingwe......"
he crooned, rubbing his big, painted head against hers,

"The time is near, yes?"
Ingwe purred aloud, so very pleased he had come.

"Indeed it is Bulala; soon, when next the jungle is filled with shadows. But it is best you are not around for the birth; you are too short-tempered for little ones, and your stomach knows no conscience! But stray not too far, dear Bulala. I fear the wild dog. They are near, for the jungle speaks loud of them. Nonya the hyaena too. Even that skulking one will attack a cat in my state! I have not long listened to his treacherous cackle reviling the jungle; indeed, I thought you were he - and I am in no fit mind to face him."

With Bulala close by Ingwe felt easier already, able to face this new experience, and whatever else that may lay ahead of her. Her sonorous purr, so like the murmur of the wind through the stout reeds flanking the great river, said as much. Bulala nudged her affectionately, before moving away toward the cave entrance, which also served as its one and only exit. On easing himself through what was no more than a long cleft in the rock, he called back to her:

"None shall enter little mother - I, Bulala, shall see to that!"
Ingwe's faith in Bulala's word was as rock solid as the granite escarpment where now she sheltered. She was lucky - few mates would wait in watch outside the den. Rest assured, she closed her eyes.

Not until the moon was well into its customary reel round the earth did she stir, catching its dewy beams in her paws as they flitted in through the cave's narrow entrance like ribbony trails of fireflies, picking out the rock and weaving spidery shadows against it. The cave was noticeably warm at night due to a release of the heat which built up in the rock during the day when, curiously, the cave was at its coolest, and thus the best place to escape to during the hotter part of the day. This

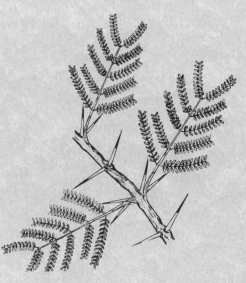

neat contradiction intrigued Ingwe, and all she could do yet again was marvel at the profound wit of Mother nature.

Since waking she had become increasingly uncomfortable. The pains were the fiercest to date. Yet the leopardess drew comfort from the realisation they brought: the moment of the birth was fast approaching. She shifted clumsily onto one side, her bulging flanks heaving in and out like fat, bulbous bellows. She drew her back legs up just as the muscles in her abdomen began to strain to the fullest, until fit, so it seemed, to squeeze every life- giving bone from her body.

Presently, no longer spasmodic, the pains grew quicker and sharper - myriad stabbing jabs that ebbed and flowed with every contraction as in in a hot, gaping wound. Fibre upon fibre of her body tightened with the moments. Time floated by unheeded. Even the sounds of her beloved jungle below the escarpment numbed into insignificance. Soon pain no longer dominated her senses either. Ingwe was conscious of a stronger phenomenon, an intangible sensation she didn't feel in the same definitive way one feels physical pain.

The big cat gasped with the shock impression of something being drawn out of her, like an earthworm from its hole; then, as though released of every strain and care, she sighed long and pleasantly. Lying between her legs was a tiny, squirming bundle. Instinctively reaching her head down, the leopardess carefully bit open the jellylike sac of tissue encasing it, and licked the newborn free, gently easing its small body into the snug curve of her own.

"Such pain for one so small......."

she murmured, nudging it tenderly. It was male, the first of three. The remaining cubs, or so it seemed to Ingwe, followed with less severity the second and third times round, and she wondered, in a wry way, if it was because they were female.....or simply that she was getting used to it. Whatever, she was pleased. Three cubs was a good litter for a leopardess in the wild. Obtaining food for a growing family is top priority for a mother, and Ingwe was confident she'd be able to provide sufficient for herself, and three cubs. After all. Her territorial area and its environs was well stocked with game; while competition from other predators was at a level with which she felt able to cope.

Nonetheless, with Bulala coming and going as he pleased - and the same with other suitors - she was all her cubs could rely upon for survival until each went their separate ways. Some mates return to the fold, sharing the family den and the task of obtaining food; even to playing a minor part in helping rear the cubs. But this is far from common practice in the jungle among leopards; especially in areas of country where their concentration was as low as it was in the wild rambling terrain encompassing Ingwe's home territory. What it really came down to was a mother's optimism and ability. It was the only truly reliable philosophy she had for the future. The rest was up to nature.

Like all newborn leopards, the cubs resembled little more than downy, grey scraps. In time they would change, as if by some wondrous trick of nature, into vigorous, patterned miniatures of Ingwe. For now their only interest, above snuggling up to Ingwe, was to suckle; and they took to this with little prompting from her - a natural enthusiasm that augured well for the future.

It wasn't until after first light, while dew still hung restive like mist over a frosty vale, that Bulala sought news of Ingwe, venturing no further than the cave's narrow entrance. On learning all was well with mate and cubs, he called back to her:

"As you rightly claim, I am too set in my ways; too impatient for ones so small and vulnerable. But I will never be far, little mother. Soon may I be with you again."

Turning, his magnificent mottled form reflecting bronze in the dawn sun, Bulala took leave of his mate, spiriting away into a solemn depth of jungle that for him held no conscious bounds.

Alone again, Ingwe pondered the future. And it was a future that was to prove the leopardess, despite her formidable ways, a devoted mother to her offspring, a quality for which leopard is renowned. Indeed, here lies one of the great contradictions of the breed. Pound for pound leopard is the jungle's most consistently successful hunter-killer - nature's ultimate *cat's-paw*.

Ingwe was no exception. Highly adaptable and patient, with ice-cool intelligence, the leopard is possessed of a ferocity so hair-raising, it can at times make a lion look mild! Yet it is capable of quite matchless tenderness as a mother. Again Ingwe was no exception. Indeed, it seemed barely credible that she could be both one and the same: an affectionate, attentive mother.....and a death-dealing virago sheathed in velvet, feared by all with a wit to live, while herself fearing little the jungle cared to set before her.

EARLY DAYS

Jaws that wrench flesh from bone,
cradle cubs gently as goose down

 ure as game quest ever onward to water along nature's weathered trails, the season passed with its customary purpose, and Ingwe's cubs grew healthy down the days. Inquisitive too, with a growing strength in form and spirit which owed as much to an innate instinct for survival common to all wild creatures, as it did to Ingwe's care and influence. The *wet* had passed its peak, and the cubs' first dry season was upon them.

Wide-eyed and kittenish, they would spend hour after carefree hour romping around the den attacking everything that wasn't attached. Bones littered about were at once foes to be stalked and leapt upon pot-bellied; or, demanding more studied concentration, dry leaves waltzing in on the wind, or sinewy columns of ants snaking across the cave, were equally irresistible lures to be promptly prodded, or patted.

Even Ingwe's stout paws, her tail as well, weren't immune, inviting lurching assaults to the constant accompaniment of little falsetto growls - cracked and vengeful! Throughout it all she would watch them with veiled gaze, knowing when to acclaim their antics, and when to chide. As always on these occasions she would be lying near the den entrance, strategically placed to keep a wary eye out for intruders, yet barely ever shifting her attention from the three cubs as they tumbled and rolled about, tousling for some highly sought after quarry in a never-ending scrum of fun.

The little females were growing, with every gala turn-out of the stars, into velvety replicas of Ingwe in ebony and amber. Only the firstborn was different. Yellow-green of eye, nature had painted him the colour of the night sky. Already bigger than either of his sisters, and with clumsy, gourd-like paws, he had the knack of looking delightfully cumbersome standing alongside the brawling, rose-tossed knot that was his sisters, anxiously awaiting his opportunity to join the fray. But easily distracted, the black cub's insatiable curiosity would often thwart patient resolve as his mind's eye would wander to something visible only to him, and away after the phantom he'd dart. Or suddenly, attracted by a flick of Ingwe's white-tipped tail, he'd at once launch an assault on that! But already schooled enough by his mother to know when to retreat, he'd be out of reach and melding flat into shadow before she could respond.

Ingwe had given much thought to the naming of the cubs. She had chosen not to rush into it, biding her time until they had grown enough to display something of their spirit and character. The smallest was in fact the gentlest of the three, and as bright and as fresh as a new bud. Ingwe loved to watch the sunrise, so she named the cub Kusasa after the glorious jungle dawn. The second little female she named Sibindi, the vital, irascible one - a cub, brimful of life and fearful of nothing, who longed to prove itself to all as the bravest of hunters.

For Ingwe, the firstborn cub, and the eldest of the three, was altogether different. He appeared to embody all those qualities the leopardess so ardently desired in

her offspring - inquisitive and alert, ever ready to learn and question, and so one with nature, he could blend with a single shadow and not be seen! Yet he was unlike anything her eyes had ever beheld.

Black, pure black as night, he glistened and shone like polished onyx. Possessing a more finely honed fierceness than Sibindi, this young one already fought with the dread fury of their kind, and even on the attack was showing signs of that indefinable leopard mystique. Carnivore supreme, the leopard is the very distillation of the perfect predator; the hunter at its peak; the quintessential cat. She dubbed him Umbulala after the one who had sired him - her mate Bulala, and still the finest hunter she yet knew - certain that of all the cubs she might bear, this one would leave a unique mark that would ring the jungle through at the merest mention of the name.......*Umbulala*. First, however, would come the learning. With the passage of the dry season, the testing time too - for mother and cub alike.

Young animals must be moved frequently, in the dry season especially. Fleas and lice are more prolific, and even the scrupulously clean leopard can do little to counter the ever-multiplying hordes of insect irritants that appear permanent, there is so many of them. But there's a reason in it all; a masterstroke in the great plan. Nature, in allowing such infernal pests to multiply and irritate, forces the big cats to regularly move. The location of a den quickly becomes known - to one hunter of the night in particular. Perhaps the most loathed of all, less for its slinking, snivelling slyness, than for the ferocity of jaws that can crush the marrow from elephant bones, the hyaena has many gifts. Most are hard to find or appreciate. But its skill at seeking out undefended cubs is exceptional. Consequently, their presence in the jungle is a constant worry to mother leopards with cubs to rear.

Ingwe was aware that the time for a move had arrived as she nibbled at one of her forelegs, crushing the life out of a lingering insect that had been nagging her since the kill. It had been nearly dawn when she had downed the duiker. Duikers of varied guises - with crests between their horns, or

17

coats that are either sleek or grizzled - frequent both open bush country, and jungle. Although only a small antelope, the cubs were still at an age when they chewed only small bits of meat. What mattered in this instance was not size, but that the kill offered essential training for the cubs in the art, and grace, of eating a meal.

Ingwe had just been in the process of lugging the carcass back to the den when she heard it: the skin-creeping giggle of hyaena coming from the direction of the den - and her cubs! Without a moment's hesitation she quickly took a firm grip of the dead buck's neck. Springing up the nearest mopane tree, she lodged it in a stout fork, streaked back down the trunk, thence away toward the den. Nimbly she cut across the top end of the valley, then up and onto the first of several large boulders leading to the thorn thicket around the den's entrance.

Leaping from boulder to boulder, from a distance the leopardess appeared more like an eagle than a cat as she gracefully flowed and glided with no less ease than the great bird itself. No big felid has the violent ferocity of the leopard. This silken force can outstrip any of its predator peers on that score - especially where offspring are concerned, and there's a glimmer of a chance of saving them. But even in this state of mind the leopard will not be foolhardy. Mother nature has endowed it with senses second to none.

Normally the heavy scent of the big male leopard Bulala, well distributed along the game path, would have put the old dog hyaena off. Nonya had indeed sensed the absence of the big cat; there had been a noticeable reduction of leopard kills in the area. But the hyaena had another problem. Although it had managed to get into the cave with relative ease in Ingwe's absence, the cubs, in an instinctive reaction to danger, had squeezed themselves into a narrow cleft between two adjacent granite slabs in the rock at the back of the den. As a result the big, spotted hyaena was stretched full-length on its hind legs, straining to push its huge snout into the crevice.

In feverish efforts to reach the cubs, saliva dribbled from its mouth, forcing the creature to gulp and lick its lips over and over, all the while, in nervous excitement, giggling and coughing in anticipation of a tender meal of young cubs. Formidable teeth slammed together as the dog's great jaws snapped at the cubs, straining to get a grip of skin or fur. But again and again the death-trap jaws snapped closed, empty, as the cubs squirmed deeper into the heart of the granite rock. For them, beyond snarls of defiance, this was no time for false heroism. If they could but hold out until Ingwe returned, all would be well! And that was just what they must do.

It was while the hyaena was in such a vulnerable position - entirely exposing its weaker rear quarters to attack from behind - that Ingwe slipped into the cave. Hearing the defiant cries of her young, the leopardess exploded in a fury of speed! She flung herself with a screaming roar at the skulking brute. Flint-sharp teeth sank deep into the hyaena, just at its shoulder blade, wrenching the beast off balance. Unsheathed, the slashing claws of her four legs dragged down the hyaena's body, ripping and cutting at every part of the old dog as it lay underneath her.

Hyaenas, even old ones, are exceptionally strong. In seconds, Ingwe's victim was on its feet with the furious cat's teeth still sunk deep into its shoulder, her claws slashing away with deadly effect. She was, after all, a leopard, one of Mother nature's master killers, and not in the best of moods. Caught off-guard, and outmatched, all that was left for the hyaena was to bolt for the den entrance. It did, throwing itself through the narrow opening - in the process, more by luck than design, striking Ingwe's face hard against the granite rock. With the pain and force of it, the leopard let go her grip. She fell to the ground, the impact on her snout making her reel and gasp for air.

The yelping of the hyaena resounded off the surrounding rock of the outcrop sheltering the cave as it fled down the hilly slope. In its panic it slipped over, losing its footing on the ground, slippery with stones and scattered rocks. Scrambling up again, it lumbered hurriedly on for fear the leopardess was in pursuit. With her snout and face still stinging from the blow, Ingwe rushed to the edge of the rocky ledge outside the den......just in time to see the scavenging dog lose its footing a second time, and tumble down over a rocky slope, its fall broken only by a tree. It was unfortunate for Nonya. The tree was the home of the wild bees - and as far as the bees were concerned they were being attacked! They swarmed after the aggressor, engulfing it and stinging it with such intensity, the hyaena threw itself against bushes and rocks and tree trunks, rolling and tossing in a frenzied bid to rid itself of the blistering horde.

"That's one hyaena that won't come sneaking around again!" grunted Ingwe, a sore but well satisfied leopard. She could have been forgiven a moment's smugness. Instead the leopardess felt subdued and chastened. Mother nature couldn't have given her a sounder lesson, she soberly told herself. At least she didn't have to hunt again immediately; and her morning's kill was well secured.

As she affectionately checked the cubs over with long, lingering licks, her mind raced through possible new dens which would make a safer haven for her young. There was, she remembered, a vast cave running higher up along the escarpment. With a couple of

narrow entrances that looked to be no more than mere slits in the rock, it was so large she'd be able to move her young around many times without breaking cover. Confident it would be as she recalled it, she would look it over. But getting to it was the drawback. She'd have to go down the face of the escarpment for a distance, then cut back up a steep slope on the other side. It wouldn't be a short, nor an easy journey. She instructed the cubs to stay well hidden while she was gone - regaling them with dire warnings about creatures who would like to eat them! She didn't have to stress the point too much. They were clearly terrified from their experience: "eyes as big as guinea-fowl eggs!" she observed amusedly as she left the den.

In the jungle, only the foolish move from place to place without care. There are many dangers, especially on a rocky escarpment that can shadow many secretive traces. Brother python, the great snake, would love such young cubs. Fortunately there were very few of real size in the area. So would baboons, creatures that delight in tearing leopard cubs apart! Then there were the great raptors; the martial eagle, in particular, which can drop like a thunderclap from the sky on the unsuspecting! A powerful bird deserving all the respect of a master hunter.

With such sombre images scurrying in and out of her thoughts to spur her on, Ingwe steadily made her way down, and around, then back up the escarpment slope towards a crest heavily encrusted with crags and crevasses. About halfway along the route she stopped to examine a fallen tree that had all the markings of having been pushed over by elephant. The roots were exposed; between them and the huge trunk was a confined area that would make a perfect lair for a leopard family on the move. She sniffed around. Part of the roots appeared to have been used as a scratching post by a rhino; the same rhino that had evidently used the soft red soil - from where the roots had been plucked - as a dust bath. In places, even the pattern of where the ponderous beast had rolled could still be seen. She marked the spot well, warning all that she, Ingwe, laid claim to it.

The journey was worth the effort.
The cave was indeed huge, and
unoccupied....apart from three large
rats which some sunrise hence would
make perfect prey for cubs learning
to hunt! There was also three well
disguised entrances, all narrow.
Ingwe concluded that the climb up to
the cave would be too difficult for
hyaena; not, however, baboon or
python. This aside, the advantages outweighed the drawbacks, and on
balance it would make an excellent den.

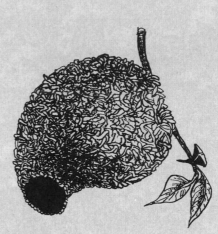

She marked the entrance areas generously to establish ownership, then set
off back to the cubs, remembering to stop and sniff around the rhino tree to
see if there had been any unwelcome visitors. None had approached. She
left fresh markings and continued on her way. She didn't, however, go
directly back to the den; she first went to retrieve her duiker kill from its snug
confines in the mopane tree where she'd safely lodged it that dawn. This
was a trying period for a mother. In moving dens, a leopardess is torn
between two places, often with a cub at either end. Ingwe thanked Mother
nature for only giving her three young; life would certainly have been
difficult with a litter of six in just providing food, let alone protecting them!

It took Ingwe between two sunrises to complete the move. Wearily carrying
the last cub up to the new den, the small creature's little body dangled like a
limp leaf in the tender grip of the mother cat's mouth; a mouth that looked
as if it could swallow the tiny head it was holding with just a gulp. Cubs
instinctively know not to twist or wriggle; a wrong move on their part could
mean a neck broken as easily as a feather bends in the breeze. Yet once
released on the cave floor it was quite another matter! Immediately it was

the signal to play as the newly arrived cub hurled herself at her brother....*he* utterly confident he couldn't be seen in the shadows!

The mother leopard sank with a sigh into the warm sunlight that pierced welcomingly through the entrance, and onto her back. The move had gone well, and she could at last relax. The cave surpassed her expectations. Cavernous and secluded, with its entrances disguised as simple clefts in a wall of rock, it was a wise choice; the climb there convincing enough of that. After all, it would be some moons to come before the cubs would be able, and old enough, to accompany her on serious hunting expeditions. Until then she would have to continue leaving them behind when she went out to hunt; otherwise, none would survive long enough to be left behind! She already felt reassured about leaving them here alone, and licking her long tail, Ingwe amused herself with thoughts of the hyaena in flight, and all of Mother nature's bees in stinging pursuit.

🐾 🐾 🐾

The leopardess stirred in the cool light of a half-awaken moon. Its eyelid had not fully opened, and wouldn't for several moonrises to come. She'd dozed a tantalisingly brief, but delicious half-slumber. It was all she could spare - unlike the cubs.......huddled together between her legs in blissful disregard of danger, sound asleep. The days when the sharp simplicities of survival wouldn't permit the luxury of such unguarded sleep were a long way off. For now, Ingwe's memory of such contentment was more a wish for her young to enjoy it while they may.

Already it was time to hunt again - less acquired wisdom, more the tell-tale pangs of hunger told her that. Mothers are expected to sleep little, work a lot; play too, and play hard if the whims of cubs are to rule! Yet, as the provider of food, Ingwe simply had to muster the energy from somewhere, anywhere - regardless. When the cubs were older it would be different. For now, everything, their very existence, depended upon her. She had no others on whom she could rely; not even Bulala. This has been the way of their kind since time immemorial.

Out front of the den, hidden as it was from searching eyes amid an innocence of rock, the clouds of the day had parted on an evening sky of deep sapphire tones. Almost glossy starling in colour, it veritably dripped stars! Like myriad silvery dewdrops slung across night's vault, they shed as much light as the moon when it was in its full circle. From beyond the rock, night's chiming choir filled Ingwe's ears. Unlike that of dawn, it was a sombrous, secret chorus befitting the caress of night....like the touch of an unseen lover.

A sound cut the subtle silence; a sound perceptible only to the most trained ear. Ingwe listened. It was an animal moving. Moments later, a gruff, yet familiar sound announced itself:

"Worry not little mother - 'tis I Bulala! I meant not to bother you. But the bee-eater told me how you and the bees settled a score with brother hyaena!"

He chuckled delightedly.

"Is all well with you?"

Ingwe called back through the rock, pleased he had sought her out:

"Bulala! All is well......and the cubs are safe."

"Then hunt with me this night little mother??"

Ingwe glanced about the den. Yes, they would be safe here. And it was indeed time for her to hunt again:

"I will, Bulala, I will!"

Ingwe checked her young, still soundly asleep. Stretching a long, snaking stretch, she again glanced around the den, taking in every detail.....thence slowly slipped out into the night.

Bulala was waiting. Ingwe rubbed her face hard against his in greeting - mate and sire of her cubs - and his scent was at once familiar and reassuring. Thus stood amid the crags of the great escarpment overlooking their jungle world, the purrs of the big cats were like the heartbeats of elephants.

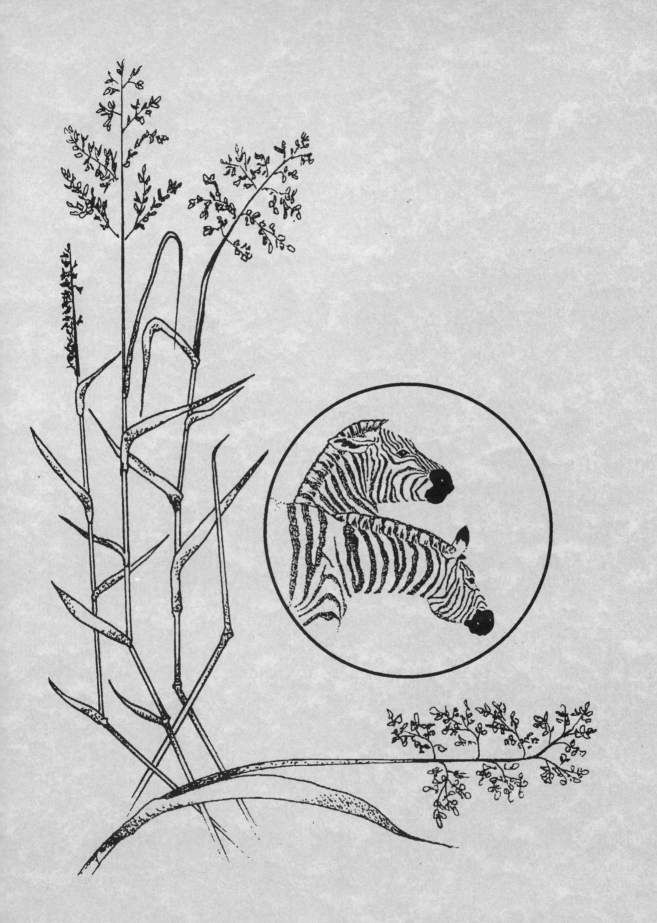

FISH AND FOWL

Scorn not the little stream,
tomorrow it could he a mighty river.

Life in the jungle is governed by two distinct and conflicting seasons, the *wet* and the *dry*, and as young animals grow to adulthood at what appears to be an extraordinarily hectic rate, by the time they have seen but three of these seasons through, cubs must seriously begin to consider leaving their mother's side to carve out a niche of their own. Some remain behind longer. But however quickly a cub may develop, the time in between is a compact and endless round of learning; preparing it ultimately for a life in the jungle it alone must forge out for itself - or perish.

Ingwe was a conscientious teacher and set aside early mornings, when the cubs were bright and willing, to lead them out on a round of exploratory hunting; leaving the more mundane, serious business of finding food for the family to the night, the ideal time to hunt in earnest. Ingwe would then venture out alone, her young remaining behind in the seclusion of the den high on the escarpment.

And so it was that the pristine delight of early morn, when the awakening jungle was stretching out fresh-winged to enfold a new day, belonged to the cubs. And so filled was it with good sport - from butterflies and grasshoppers, to lizards and frogs, squirrels and mice - to the cubs it must have seemed as if Mother nature had arranged it specifically for them! Indeed, there could be no better time for eager cubs to learn.

To the anxious-faced little trio, anything that slithered, hopped, scampered or flew was potential prey set aside just for cubs. Of course, a good deal of the time, certainly to begin with, they were too full of cubbish exuberance to have much success in most, if not all, their forays. Only when they were three, perhaps four full moons old did they seem able to overcome their youthful impatience a little, notably with guinea-fowl. At the edge of a waterhole or secluded pool, behind rocks hidden beneath a froth of fern and grass, the cubs would lie in wait for a jabbering covey to come down to drink.......the cleverly developed floating collarbones of the little cats allowing them to lay as flat and motionless as lichen.

Guinea-fowl are quite the most feather-brained of jungle birds, a fact not entirely unrelated to the unpredictability of the environment they live in! They jump and squawk at the slightest movement or whisper of sound, noisily pounding off down a game trail at a frenetic pace - behaviour that invariably makes them, in the eyes of any cat, a temptation impossible not to chase and despatch from this world! With delicately spotted white on black plumage hitched high above two, stick-like legs that would work the ground furiously as they scurried away - blue and red wattles wobbling, and protesting indignantly *chit-tchirr-tchirrrrr* - the cubs found them an irresistible tease.

Despite nifty tricks like flushing out tasty insects by upturning stones with a flick of a small horn on the top of their head, guinea-fowl give little allusion to cleverness, and were forever being caught unawares by Umbulala and his sisters; usually when fussily pecking and prattling their way down to a

waterhole in a swarm of feathers and busyness.

Then, as always, Ingwe would be watching from a nearby vantage point, lying lazily stretched out along the branch of a well-foliaged tree - a bountiful ebony, or a rambling fig. She was a relaxed teacher. She didn't believe in examining the cubs every move, preferring to let them obtain as much practical experience as they could, with her close-by to prevent anything untoward happening. This, and learning by minor mistakes, was how cubs were best taught the ways of the jungle. But where she never let slip her guard was in keeping a constant vigil for signs of any threat to their safety. Hence the importance of a good look-out.

A sure indicator to Ingwe of just how the cubs had fared in bushwhacking some unfortunate beast would the degree of dust thrown up! Sometimes in a clash at a waterhole with a couple of francolin - the quail of the bush - it wasn't uncommon for Ingwe to see, once the air had cleared, Kusasa and Sibindi playing tug-of-war with the same wretched bird, neither showing any intention of letting go - the jaws of one cub wrapped firmly round the fowl's dislocated neck, the teeth of the other dug deep into a wing. Umbulala, his mouth a picture of feathers, would be elsewhere, crouched four-square over the headless corpse of a second bird, its dismembered part lying some distance away in the water......a vulgar, disconsolate blur running red.

At each clumsy confrontation Ingwe could only sigh and look on as the cubs ate their fill. Later she might go through the traces with them, reassuring herself that just as the jungle orchid must first blossom right out before its full worth is known, so too, in time, would Umbulala and his sisters. After all, cubhood is little more than a tremor across the strings of time; a jumbled note of excitement and confusion condensed into one brief interval, no longer than four seasons of life. But although free of serious responsibility and challenge, understanding this complex state of being that it has been born into is responsibility enough for any young predator! What's more, the

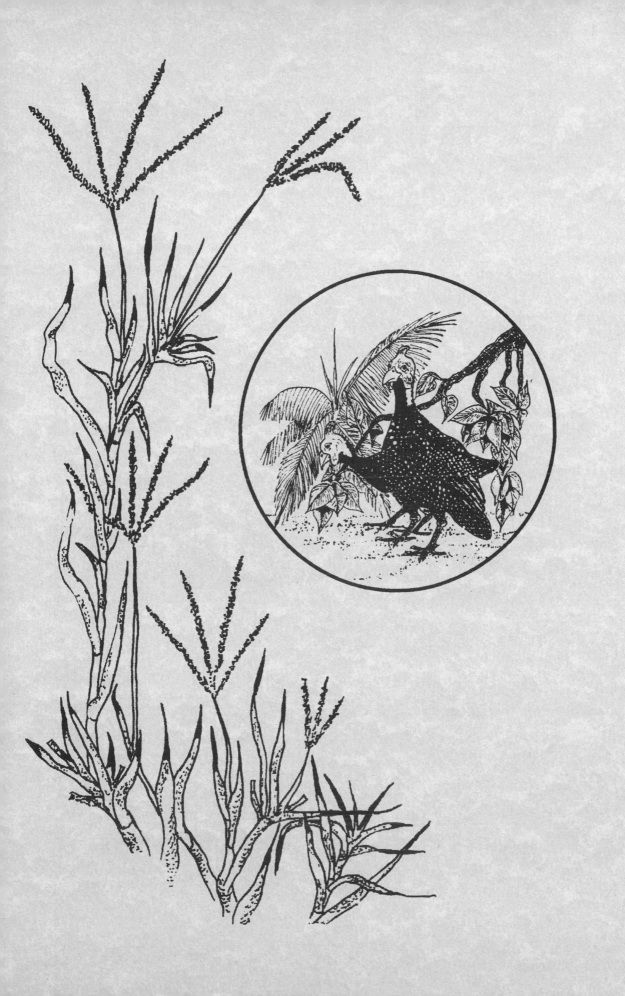

amount of learning a cub is confronted with over such a contracted space of time is the only basis for survival it is ever going to receive.

Once, when the cubs were down by the great waterhole trying in vain to catch themselves a bullfrog, Umbulala happened upon a tiny, luminous bird perched on the topmost tip of a tree root jutting out of the lagoon where the bank had eroded away. So small, and so iridescent blue was it, shimmering in the waving sunlight reflected off the water, that Umbulala could have been forgiven for mistaking it for a speck of sky......had it not dived into the depths, and quickly out again with a fish in its beak. Returning immediately to its perch - doubtless a favourite vantage point from which to survey the surrounding reaches of the lagoon - it proceeded to heartily *thwack* the unhappy fish against the wood to soften it, before swallowing it whole; head-first, naturally, so that the scales lay "just so".

Totally unexpectedly, the small bright creature suddenly turned its attention to the black cub, watching engrossed from the bank.

"Well, well, little Umbulala! I see you haven't yet mastered, as we kingfishers have, the art of catching water creatures! But don't be distressed - I'm told that, like the crocodile, the frog too tastes foul!"

Umbulala shuddered with embarrassment. He'd never thought his misadventures frog-hunting had been that obvious!

The tiny, blue-green bird, a malachite kingfisher - sparkling, for all the world, like a sapphire in the bosom of Mother earth - plunged off again into the shining pool, this time re-emerging atop a water lily pad a little way beyond the papyrus. Flashing a chest the colour of sunset, it returned at once to its perch on the tree root, just skimming the surface of the water; another silver-backed fish twinkling in its orange beak. Politely, Umbulala waited until it had eaten. The inquisitive cub then asked the malachite if it knew where the water came from as he, Umbulala, wished to know all things. The little bright bird gazed abstractedly at some far off ripples. It pondered a moment, then thoughtfully replied:

"It is said that the river is a scar in
Mother earth.......a scar from which
she weeps constantly for the needs
and deeds of her children, birds and
animals - all living creatures."

A feeling of disquiet ran through the
black cub.

"And the rain?"

"Ah....the rains - they are the tears
of Mother nature.....crying for her sister, Mother earth."

It was a solemn tale, one the cub hadn't expected, and he felt strangely
chastened, though he was sure he had never wilfully done anything to hurt
Mother earth. The malachite appeared not in the least perturbed. Uttering a
shrill *peep-peep*, it darted off again at speed to catch another fish before
Umbulala could thank it for sharing its wisdom, grave as it was.

Sighing quietly to himself, the cub repaired to the water's edge for a drink.
To be sure, he was too young to be feeling the guilt of the world. His mind
thus occupied, all thought of danger washed from it, he stumbled on
distractedly into a tall stand of grass. As high as a heron, it swallowed the
little cat utterly from view. Just then, as he came up under a spreading
waterberry tree, a voice - strange and new to him - called out from somewhere
overhead, startling him:

"Whoa, little hunter of the night! Why do you approach death-silent
clutches so eagerly; especially one so young?"

Umbulala froze in his tracks. Two shocks in one day was too much! Bright,
frantic eyes, like two full moons, feverishly scanned the branches overhead.
But only a silence of foliage and branch looked down at him. All a-quiver,
the cub suddenly felt very alone - and the chill certainty that he couldn't see
his mother, either, gripped him!

Again the tree called down to him:

"I too am a hunter. Yet though unlike you in shape, one thing I have learned to my benefit is the importance of observing well before proceeding."

The tone was husky and forbidding.

"Only fools strike out in reckless abandon....and it usually marks their doom!"

The little cat shuddered as a dreadful fear ran through him. He was at an utter loss as to what to do! Caterwauling would attract his mother's attention; but it was so unseemly......and before he had a chance to think more on it the voice in the tree came back to taunt him, calling down sharply:

"My prey can prove as difficult to catch as the creatures your kind feeds on! And mine......."

the voice suddenly softened,

"are only insects! So heed well my advice little panther. Observe every detail of Mother nature's many and varied faces, for it is usually in the most unexpected places that Brother error awaits the unwary!"

With a deftness of movement that very nearly defied description, and which lizards of its ilk have mastered to impressive effect, a chameleon all at once materialised before Umbulala's eyes. From the very leafage itself, so it seemed to the cub! Certainly one of the most grotesque creatures to have pop out in front of one - just like that - the little cat's eyes darted from his head! Fortunately he'd heard tell that chameleons were no enemy of leopards, even little ones like him, and Umbulala breathed an audible sigh of relief.

According to his mother they were very clever. But he would never have believed just how clever if he hadn't seen it for himself. To change colour like that! Almost in the time it takes to blink! Umbulala wasn't too sure he hadn't seen it change shape as well, so ably did this brother quicksilver move along the flimsiest of twigs and leaves with little clamp-like feet, and a long serpentine tail which gripped so efficiently it was practically an extra limb.

The bulbous, scaly-lidded eyes appeared to be everywhere at once - and the cub marvelled, for even as the creature gazed down at him, it simultaneously stalked a dewy-winged dragonfly on the branch above. Indeed, he could have sworn its eyes had a life of their own! Even as one eye rolled around full circle to look down at him, the other rolled in the direction of the dragonfly above, at which the chameleon shot out a tongue as long as itself, pinned the insect down - then whisked it straight into its frog-like mouth.

"You see, little one, how well I observe? Hence I warn you - go any nearer the water's edge and the crocodile lurking there will have a feast of black cub!"

Weelll!! Umbulala may still have been a novice, and a very young one at that, but he was a good listener and knew when not to flaunt advice sincerely given. At the mention of the dreaded crocodile, every hair of his polished hide bristled from end to end.....and like lightning bouncing off water, he lifted off the ground in that stiff-legged, fur-perpendicular cat's way, skidded up the tree trunk, and onto a branch firm enough to hold him in the beat of a bat's wing!

When at last his little heart ceased beating against his chest like a demented woodpecker, and a degree of calm had returned to his senses, Umbulala noticed that the tree afforded him a fine view of the waterhole for some distance up and down its immediate bank. Peering down, his eyes fell on the strip of water alongside of which, but moments before, he'd been walking. It had none of the sparkle and glimmer of that part

of the lagoon where he'd met with the kingfisher; nor where he'd been playing with his sisters, who by now would be wondering where on earth he'd got to! Umbulala cringed at the thought of his carelessness and what they would say to him, especially Sibindi! But he really couldn't think about that now. For the moment a far bigger concern, one with monstrous jaws and teeth, was demanding his attention!

In comparison to the rest of the pool, the patch of water in question looked desolate and murky, as if the very shadow of Brother death had fallen over it. Umbulala shivered, suddenly feeling very grateful for his leafy sanctuary, and the timely warning given him by the chameleon, somewhere behind him still blissfully swatting insects. Umbulala had heard that crocs can breathe with just the merest snip of nostril winking above the waterline; this, along with a protruding pair of stony eyes, is often the only outward indication one is around. They can even resemble little more than logs floating idly on the water. They can accelerate astonishingly quickly, too! In a short rush out of water, crocodiles can move as fast as the fleetest antelope - like a green blur in the blinking of an eye.

Umbulala wasn't taking any more chances. From his safe hide in the waterberry, his sharp eyes honed in on two mossy-brown lumps, lying side by side on the surface of the water. He riveted his gaze on the spot. Not a ripple betrayed a presence. Yet the cub needed no sixth sense to tell him what those secretive, ominous protrusions, and the sinister sluggard lurking beneath meant for any unsuspecting animal coming down to drink. Crocodiles are the master killers of river and lagoon, eating almost anything they can catch. Ancient monsters that have remained virtually unchanged since before the giant lizards departed these earthly tracts aeons back, they are cunning and immensely powerful, of awe-inspiring reflex - and abiding patience.

But leopards, too, are very, very patient; perhaps the most patient of all the cats. And, young and inexperienced as he was, Umbulala began to draw on

that quality; a quality as inherently natural to his kind as those skills that make the leopard the greatest of the jungle's hunters. He watched. Still the crocodile remained motionless; hidden, except for a nose-tip and two eyes - a beast suspended incongruous with the beauty of a watery dell swathed in water lilies of the most gentle cast and colours. Nothing stirred, nothing sang around that clutch of water as cat and crocodile waited, time a blur across consciousness.

Finally, after what seemed an eternity of seasons, signs of crocodile began to slip silently beneath the surface of the water. Nary a ripple disturbed it - just the tell-tale trail of water lilies bobbing in and out of the reptile's wake as it glided away, deeper and deeper into the lagoon on course for darker tracts where no water lilies grew, and no welcome haven awaited the unwary. Umbulala had long forgotten his thirst, and even with the passing of what for a cub was no fanciful chimaera, nothing could entice him down to the water's edge! Glancing furtively around, he saw that the chameleon was still there:

"Mother nature has given you much wisdom brother chameleon....."
the cub addressed the lizard gratefully,

"may she protect you, as you have me this day!"

Umbulala felt immensely grown-up. After all - he had lived a lifetime this day! But such feelings can be short-lived, often being little more than borrowed plumes. For never was there a cub more keen to get back to romping with his sisters; nor one more hungry for the warmth and comfort only his mother could give him.

JUNGLE LORE

*Dragonflies search the river
for twins the fish swallowed*

The three little leopards had developed well since birth. With each passing of the moon, Ingwe watched cubhood fade until the time finally came when she no longer felt the need to worry constantly for their welfare. Now, on occasion, she could turn her mind to musings far removed from the mundane routine of family life - although the litter was always within the safe bounds of her reach! At such times, with perhaps the cubs snugly ensconced up a nearby tree sunning their stout little stomachs, she might lie up dreamily in some vulture's nest, or steal a quick nap stretched out along the friendly bough of a nearby tree. Unmolested by cubs tousling to snuggle up to her, such rest to a predator - and a busy and active mother - is paramount if a long and healthy existence for mother and family alike is to be sustained.

Thus, in the cool quiet of some snatched moment's solitude, life was deliciously her own again with the rigours and regimen of teaching temporarily thrown off. Yet it wasn't always lessons that would so demand her attention. Like leopard mothers the jungle over, Ingwe was a regular and eager participant in the games of her cubs, especially as they grew bigger. And not just as a spectator - but pawing, chasing and generally gambolling about with them as if she were little more than a cub herself! Hence moments of complete repose were all too often short-lived. Meanwhile, those days when Ingwe could claim sole responsibility for deciding where and when she would take the cubs for a round of exploration-cum-hunting were also fast slipping away. Times were that she wasn't even given a choice!

Like the day, at the cubs behest, she found herself wending her way behind them along a shadowy game trail toward a distant vlei - a kind of shallow, swampy depression, or watery meadow, which is a sea of small animal life in the *wet*. Bringing up the rear, where she could keep them well in view while remaining alert to danger, Ingwe was surprised to see the cubs suddenly scurry ahead.

A few elephant paces on along the path, a dead mopane tree knocked across it had caught the cub's attention. It was clearly the work of elephant; now, for better for worse, it was an objective to be laid siege to by the cubs! Kusasa led the charge, gliding as effortlessly as a water skimmer up the angled trunk, and on to where a spindly clutter of gnarled roots stood gaunt against the sky. Without any provocation Ingwe could see, the little spotted cat immediately arched her back, fell into a crouch, and spread herself lengthwise along the trunk of the mopane, flat as her cub-plump belly would allow.

Slipping alongside the fallen tree towards where its roots lay like a giant, withered claw wrenched from the earth, Ingwe at once saw what Kusasa was stalking. The leopardess hastened to caution her cub:

"That's no easy prey little one! Good food I grant you. But be warned - Brother warthog is not to be tampered with; especially one as this, who has lived to see many seasons through."

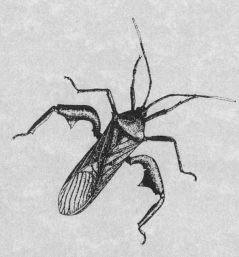

An odd-looking animal, with the equally odd habit of kneeling down on its two front legs to grub for roots, Ingwe's words were given added potency when the

warthog sprung up and wheeled round to face the cubs - now all crouched flank to flank atop the tree root, their bright, startled eyes stretched wide as morning glories. They had never come face to face with anything quite like it before! Thick matted callouses caked the hog's knees like limpets. Its head seemed ill-proportioned, gnarled and rough-hewn like weather-beaten rock, with warty nodules either side of its face below each eye, and lower down the snout. There was about this warthog the air of a hardened veteran, lent something by the large tusks protruding from its jowls, the hoary whiskers, and a scraggly mane of long, stiff hairs hanging limp and loose from its neck and shoulders. With few pretensions to grace or beauty, it looked the very epitomc of piggish ill-humour.

"Those tusks......"

Ingwe whispered hurriedly to the cubs, endeavouring not to antagonise the old boar,

> "especially the long ones curving up from the sides of its mouth like gigantic talons, are used to dig up roots, with the shorter ones underneath acting as cutters. Hence they are very sharp and strong - and can rip cubs wide open if they're not careful!!"

Conjuring up the picture, the cubs eyes nearly popped from their sockets.

"Such weapons...."

Ingwe added purposefully as she continued to appraise the warthog's appearance and prowess,

> "make the warthog a formidable opponent you are well-advised to think twice about before tackling!"

With a leopardess and her entire family looking him up and down, the old warthog didn't view his situation with the same degree of equanimity! After all, these cats had a definite predilection for eating warthog. Rcversing backwards, he scuttled tailfirst down an antbear hole - he'd appropriated earlier - so to give him the advantage if pursued. Meeting head on, an

aggressor ran the risk of being torn
apart by the hog's treacherous
tusks. Ingwe proceeded to warn the
cubs with a solemn shake of her
head:

"Young warthog can be rash
and full of boasts, making them
easy prey.   But of the big
tuskers - those that have lived
to see many seasons pass, and have been known to face even lion -
beware my little ones!"

Ingwe continued on along the game path toward the vlei - the cubs now
securely in tow. Already the heat of late morning had begun to penetrate the
bush canopy, and the party was still some distance from the nearest available
water when the cubs began to tire; the younger two growing noticeably
irritable with each another. There was only one cure for it that Ingwe knew.
Some harmless fun.

With a conspiratorial glance at little Umbulala, the leopardess urged the
cubs to keep up as suddenly, stepping up the pace, she veered off the path to
slip effortlessly away through a maze of scrub. With mother and big brother
spiriting off like that, all notions of discomfort were forgotten. In the flash
of a swallow's wing, Kusasa and Sibindi hastened away after them. The big
wild world of jungle, with its unpredictable cut and thrust, is no place for
young leopards who, with a penchant for living, can't keep up the pace!
Hyaena, for one, are not impartial to a light breakfast of cub to give the start
to the day a little added zest.

The big mottled cat moved ahead with all the satiny grace of a dancing
gazelle. Her patterned form melded and weaved through a tapestry of
greenery like a brocade flicker, rising and falling in the light and the dappled
shadows towards an eruption of a tree - a tree that to the untrained eye just

seemed to loom up out of nowhere. All the cubs could focus on with any accuracy in the meantime was the white tip of Ingwe's upright tail, bobbing along ahead of the them in the greenery like a guiding star.

As his mother neared the giant tree, Umbulala caught sight of it for the first time. It was a baobab, a mighty *upside-down-tree*, and its weird, gaunt shape, and fearful, writhing branches silhouetted against the sky, made for a sight macabre enough to turn any black cat white with fright! In a lithe bound Ingwe scaled the gigantic trunk. Finding a comfortable perch, she settled down to watch the approaching antics of her cubs. She had nestled in the bosom of the tree, the very heart of the baobab, where great stony branches reached on up towards the sun from atop a bizarre, swollen trunk that looked as wide around as an elephant is long!

This particular baobab was an old and venerable friend, having sustained and accommodated Ingwe on many occasions. In fact, it was a welcome haven for birds and animals too numerous to number, and had probably seen as many seasons pass as the old crocodile down at the rock pool where the hippos lived. In its topmost branches predatory birds like hawks, owls and eagles nested - great raptors that never appeared to prey on the smaller birds that came and went on the lower branches! Perhaps it was nature's very own code of chivalry; a code which seems to have as much courteous regard for jackals, as it has for heaven-blessed steenboks, slender, sharp-witted little antelopes that live alone.

Unfortunately for the baobab, elephants were also keenly attracted to it. There was something about the great tree's bark that they craved, resulting in ugly wounds being left behind on the trunk. Baboons, too, were regular visitors. They had a singular passion for its hard, woody cream-of-tartar pods. Catching sight of one, Ingwe sneered:

"HUMPH! Those ugly monkeys only wait until others have had their fill before moving in to finish off the dregs!"

Baboons were not among Ingwe's favourite fellow creatures. Indeed, nothing failed to raise her hackles more than the sight, sound or thought of baboons; a feeling mutual among leopards.

Sibindi and Kusasa caught up with their big brother at the base of the baobab - and both were as awestruck as Umbulala at their first sight of it! Despite leopards learning to climb from a tender age, it was a fact that appeared to be foiling their very attempts to scramble up it! In between caterwauling, and numerous solicitous urgings from Ingwe, they kept falling down, one on top of the other, in a wriggling, squalling heap, with each cub convinced it was the brunt of some brutal, furtive attack from behind.

"Come now, concentrate...!"
Ingwe admonished them,

"There could well be a wild dog leering behind that bush to the back of you. Or worse still - an hyaena!"

Ingwe's reverse cub psychology worked like a charm. In no time at all the three cubs scaled the tree in one, not putting a velvet-sheathed paw wrong. To their astonishment they found a well of water in the centre of the baobab where its huge branches, bigger than elephant's legs, converged to meet the trunk. Umbulala immediately crouched to drink, as did his 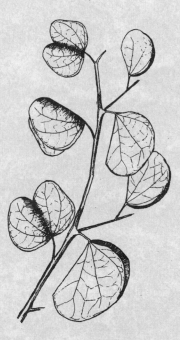 sisters; looking for all the world like the furled petals of the jungle orchid their tiny pink tongues lapped the cool traces, neatly curling to catch the precious liquid as a flower cups the dew.

Presently refreshed following their enlivening drink, the three cubs each chose a branch to stretch out along, joining mother in like repose; her stout limbs and tail dangling in idle abandon either side of her chosen support.

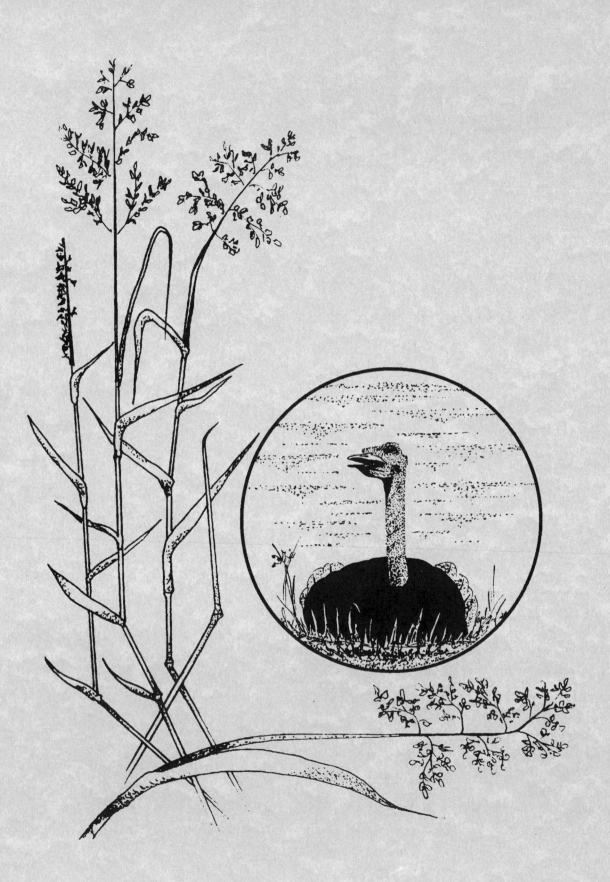

Umbulala drowsily gazed at her through half-closed eyes, mewling something about how thoughtful it was of Mother nature to put a pond way up in a tree just for them. Ingwe stretched lazily, tensing her shoulders. Extending her forelegs out along the branch, she began to knead abstractedly as if trying to conjure up some remote reminiscence. Strong, pristine-white claws gripped and wrenched at the wood. Scoring and cutting with the ease of scalpels, they dragged along the limb, biting long incisions deep into the bark until it bled.

"It's a long story little Umbulala........"

she at last remarked, bringing an immediate response from the cubs who straightaway shook off all vestiges of sleep to listen intently.

"Now Mother nature has a special affection for things of a refined and gentle beauty - like the multi-faced flowers, and the butterflies and bees that fuss about them. There was one quiet spot in the jungle she called her own, and here grew every conceivable kind of blossom: finely scented, and so abounding in nectar, the place was a haven for a wealth of carpenter bees, mayflies, swallowtails and the like. Once while abroad here, her attention was aroused by a very disconsolate bee who exclaimed that the flowers were dying!

"It seemed that once, where there had been many to furnish a bounty of insects competing for their charms, only one kind now flourished. And it was to the detriment of all the other flowers. Being only a small, insignificant hive bee, the poor creature couldn't get near even a petal! Mother nature resolved to examine the matter. When she did, she found to her dismay that the tale was true. All the plants were withering - except for the baobab. By contrast it was in full bloom, and thriving..........just as it is today, with its large white flowers like cloud-bursts, a-tremble with a multiplicity of pampering insects.

"Such a state both worried and
perplexed Mother nature as it left
her with a feeling of helplessness
she had never known before; a
feeling only compounded by her
loss to understand how the
situation could
ever have arisen in the first place.
Had she not endeavoured to
engender instincts of harmony
and moderation in all living creatures? She determined to get to the
bottom of it, demanding of Mother earth an immediate explanation.

"Her poor sister was in a terrible state of distress. It seems she had been
providing all the plants with as much food and goodness as they needed
to thrive and multiply, let alone grow. But the greedy, overbearing
baobab had developed a large bulb under the soil - somewhat the shape
of a calabash pod - from which it stretched out a tangled web of grasping,
guzzling roots to overrun the roots of other plants, virtually suffocating
them, and thereby taking all the soil's goodness for itself. This deeply
pained Mother nature. In her heart of hearts she loved the wilful baobab;
moreover, she delighted to see, as the cloying sparseness of the long dry
season drew to a close, its beautiful flowers, massed in snowy radiance,
heralding the spring.

"Seizing hold of the plant, she plucked it from Mother earth, ripping away
its fibrous gossamer of roots until all that remained was a bevy of long,
tuberous growths bearing a striking resemblance to elephant trunks. 'Oh
you wicked plant!', she cried, plunging it back headfirst into the ground,
'may you forever be an example to the greedy of the jungle - planted
upside down in Mother earth, with your roots dangling ridiculously
skyward!' It thus became the baobab's turn to discover what necessity

and hardship was, just like those plants it had cheated of what was rightfully theirs.   Now it would have to learn what, on the face of it, looked an impossible task - and that was to

grow its branches downwards as roots.......and its roots upwards as branches!

"Mother nature further told it: 'Through suffering you will learn compassion, flourishing into the largest of jungle trees so that all may come to know of the mighty baobab and partake of its shelter and sustenance.   In your heart of branches there will nest a placid pool of water that will be an oasis for all the thirsty followers of the air, and those climbing creatures that care to find it; while to others you will give forth fruit aplenty to eat.   You will live longer than any other tree of the jungle, and every season of new bud will array yourself before nature in a pageant of flowers containing nectar enough for bee and bluebottle alike'."

Ingwe sighed, as with a final pungent twist to the tale, she concluded:

"The flowers, favoured as much by the little galagos as they are by the bluebottles, were destined to only ever open at night - bearing a scent neither sweet-breathed nor honey-spiked, but one forever tainted with the odour of carrion."

SEASON's SHADOW

The greatest hunter eclipses not the flower

It was a peerless sun-shot afternoon. Ingwe and the cubs had not long taken refuge from the rigours of the hunt in amongst some leafy branches of a handsome mahogany tree, the breeze tossed spread of its glittering crown cool balm against the heat. The cubs had grown a great deal and were now well on their way to seeing in their first seasonal cycle in the jungle.

Before long Kusasa became restless for a little adventure. A small, sun-kissed clearing caught her eye. It looked deliciously enticing and at once a sense of mischief took her over:

"Hmmmmm....I can certainly rustle up some fun there..!!"
her thoughts sang, and leaving the safety of the tree, the cub scurried down. Ingwe sighed as she watched her go. Slowly but surely her little ones were casting off the skin of cubhood. Even so, that special capacity for enjoyment unique to cats still held sway.

In no time at all Kusasa was having the time of her life, darting every which way, cuffing and sniffing at the air, and launching mock attacks on clumps of malopo grass and anything else scattered about that took her fancy. At one stage her keen eyes, with a cubbish look of devilment so characteristic of cats at play, lighted on a musk shrew. Although she'd long outgrown such small prey, she felt she couldn't pass up a chance to show off her hunting skills to Umbulala and Sibindi, still ensconced in their lofty perch. Both had a tendency to pet her because she was smaller and less serious than them; although to be fair, Umbulala, quite the strong silent type who at times could be as much full of fun as she, was never openly condescending, and she adored him for it. Not that she felt she wasn't as capable a hunter as the next cub! Quite the contrary.

Crouching low, her prettily painted head as pointed and straight as a snake in ambush, her ears hard-flat against it, she began to stalk the shrew, taking care not to move a hair of her mottled hide, nor avert her gaze from her tiny quarry by even a whisker. Nearer she crept, rapier-sharp. Her body, belied only by the flickery tip of her tail, twitched not so much as a muscle until, judging to be within range, she pounced. But the shrew winded her - scampering down a hole hardly big enough to fit a tuft of grass!

As yet unaware she'd been outfoxed, Kusasa slowly half lifted one front paw, then the other, and shyly and stealthily peered under each in turn, positive she had the shrew trapped; her head poised in a classic arc of feline expectancy. But.........no shrew! Kusasa was aghast!! Eyes wide with questions, she darted confused looks around her, then back to her paws again, now fitfully groping the ground in jerky search-and-destroy movements that only served to annoy her further by dashing bits of grass and dust into her face. Thwarted by a shrew indeed! Suddenly she remembered her family.

Had they seen what had happened? She caught her breath in horror at the thought of it. The cub cast a furtive glance over each shoulder. Then, adjusting her expression to one of casual indifference, she got up.....and slowly proceeded to stroll away in that nonchalant, loose-limbed

swagger of cats; her tail curved haughtily upward as if the suggestion of chasing a shrew was simply too vulgar to be contemplated!

The jungle harbours many eyes that go unseen by the unwary. One such pair was now watching Kusasa, back to the game of mock-charging imaginary adversaries. It was old Kosi: an ailing, rangy lion who, some moons previous, had come off the worse for wear in a chance encounter with a porcupine that had been innocently waddling its way down a game path from the opposite direction. A prickly character boasting formidable reflexes when confronted, the porcupine is one animal with which the prudent predator is better advised not to clash! It reacts with lightning speed, spinning around full-circle within its own length to offer a bristling defence in a bouquet of spike-tipped quills that makes it virtually impregnable.

Being too proud to give way to what, in Kosi's view, was a wholly unworthy opponent for one such as he, Kosi attacked - only to receive in return for his bluster a splinter-sharp quill deep inside his mouth. Piercing both the upper and lower jaws, it caused irreparable damage, resulting in the most excruciating pain; so great it made the lion's eyes water. As a consequence he could no longer hunt normally. Prime game, such as buffalo and large antelope, were now beyond him.

Instead he had to resign himself for food to small animals, duiker for instance; even guinea-fowl and similar creatures that could be eaten in small bites. Only in this way could the lion keep the pain to a minimum. In this wretched state it was of some help that, being blessed with the lion's uncommonly rough tongue, he was able to lick away complete layers of flesh with little effort. All the same, life for Kosi was a misery, and understandably, with no respite from the constant, searing pain inside his mouth, it left him very bad-tempered. Even in sleep he had no escape. He'd unconsciously move his mouth, and the quill would force itself deeper into the festering gums. Not only that. For as big a cat as a lion, forced to subsist on such a meagre diet of small animals, Kosi's appetite was never satisfied.

Thus the old lion was constantly hungry......and here was a plump leopard cub just ripe for the eating!

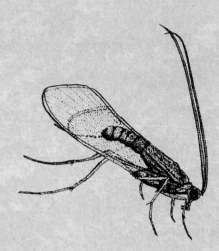

Kosi erupted from the thick cover concealing him, and in one bound killed Kusasa with a massive clout from a forepaw; every bone in her chest shattering like a mosaic. As death shrouded her silken fleece, there escaped at the moment of impact a single cry:

"UUUMMBULLAAAAaaaa!"

The sound of death shakes the senses of the living like nothing else. Inexpressibly sad, it resounded across the clearing and away into the jungle like a solemn report of thunder.

In a heartbeat, the leopard family in the mahogany tree sprung to attention as one.....just at the moment Kosi emerged from behind a strapping stand of elephant grass - the lifeless body of Kusasa hanging limp from his decrepit jaws. Emaciated as Kosi was, it didn't make for a pretty sight. Powerless to do anything, the leopardess snarled and spat at him, her hopeless fury seeming almost to drip in blood from her lips. There was little else she could do. Delightful, fun-loving Kusasa, the smallest of her young, was dead; a fait accompli that, amid the capricious vicissitudes of jungle life, she could ill afford to contest. The ragged lion turned his full gaze on the leopard family, now facing him foursquare from the mahogany tree, and spluttered:

"Let this be a lesson to you all for crossing my path. Indeed you mother leopard have hunted too long in my territory. Why.....!"

he continued with all the arrogance of his kind,

"before the next rainy season has worn itself out, I will have feasted on all three of your fat, stupid cubs!!"

It was Umbulala, not Ingwe, who broke the ensuing silence; a silence that cloyed and choked the very air it clung to. Slithering forward along the branch he'd hitherto been lying along, he delivered a stinging riposte destined to set the jungle agog in eager anticipation for moons to come:

"Before that time I, Umbulala, will have killed you, oh slayer of cubs, worms and slugs. But of your flesh I will not eat, for fear it may poison me as it has you! Instead, I shall do with it what it deserves - leave it as scrap for the scavengers of the jungle!"

Many moons back Kosi had heard that Ingwe had given birth the previous rainy season to three cubs by Bulala - just three more potential competitors for food, he'd wearily thought at the time. But this was the first he'd seen of them. It was also the first time he had ever set eyes upon a black leopard! Although still an adolescent, this cat already looked twice as big as his sisters, and not far from being even a match in size for his mother; his sable-black coat shining with health.

Umbulala's chilling yellow eyes rifled through the foliage, and as sinewy shafts of sunlight danced through the breeze tossed leaves to pick out the polished sheen of his shadowy form, it may well have seemed to the old lion that the very apparition of the messenger of death had come to call! Here was no normal leopard, and Kosi shuddered. He gave vent to a savage roar he hoped might alter the panther's mind. But Umbulala didn't even flinch........and Kosi cursed the pain in his mouth as he slunk back into the undergrowth, Kusasa's body dangling irreverently from his jaws.

Ingwe maintained a degree of calm, expressing her thoughts with a chilly acceptance:

"Kusasa is dead!"

If the family was to survive it was an acceptance she must sustain.

"And if we cannot learn from it, it will truly be a waste. In the jungle, life is as precious as we wish to make it. We must always keep our ears and eyes open, seeing all and missing nothing, however it might displease us. Hence you must always be ready, little ones, to learn from the mistakes of others so that in time you may avoid Brother error's traps. Just because you are strong and healthy of body doesn't mean that you may arrogantly wander the seasons through without restraint or care. If this much had been true of Kosi, he would not now be the scavenging reminder of the lion he once was, with Brother death stalking his shadow. All of us in the jungle, from the humblest shrew....."

Ingwe motioned towards the clearing, now scuffed and sadly deserted,

"to the mightiest elephant can be the greatest of hunters, and as such as arrogant as we wish! Especially if fortunate to be counted among the great predators like Kosi's kind.....and ours!"

Ingwe sighed, hoping they might understand this much at least.

"But it will be as nothing if we don't accord that power with which we have been invested by Mother nature the respect and delicacy it deserves. *Never* attack a porcupine little ones - it is the act of a foolish cat, not a master hunter. Brother and Sister porcupine also have their greatness - they can deal well enough with lion, after all! All deserve respect - if for no other reason than your own survival."

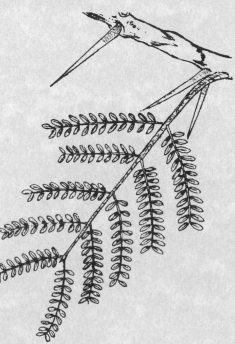

Ingwe gazed at her two remaining cubs, more precious to her than ever, thence wistfully away into space, now found wanting of something, her primrose yellow eyes not without their touch of sadness.

It was awhile after Kusasa's tragic end, as another long

forbidding dry steadily approached, that Umbulala was marked by yet another experience he would long remember. Nonchalantly spread-eagled along the doughty branch of an acacia tree, all four legs dangling limply, the young panther was alone; Ingwe and Sibindi were elsewhere, stalking up a snack. Without warning, the singular, sawing cough of a full-grown leopard filtered across the sleepy haze of afternoon. Like so much else about their kind, it came from nowhere.....yet everywhere. It was not familiar. It was not his mother. And it occurred to Umbulala that a leopard that could conceal its position so well was without doubt one of those master hunters she'd oft told him about.

The young panther lay completely still, all his senses working simultaneously. Another soughing cough, then out into an opening just beyond the acacia emerged a leopard bigger than any Umbulala had ever imagined: one with the stamp of veteran written across every rosette of its hide! A big powerful male, he plopped down with a muffled grunt. Umbulala did his level best to dissolve into the tree's shadows with which he melded so well. The big spotted leopard curled his tail around him, turned and lifted his head - and gazed directly up at the black cat! Valiantly puffing himself up, Umbulala snarled, grandiosely displaying his fangs in an attempt to warn off the intruder. He had a distinct feeling, however, that this big stranger wasn't going to be put off by any boast. Anyway, he'd already noted - with some relief - that the lower branches of the tree couldn't possibly hold the bigger cat.

For what seemed moons, the two cats stared towards one another - the younger cat an unsprung, unsung coil of predatory potential; the other, the ultimate evolution of the jungle carnivore, predator consummate. It was the elder of the two leopards that finally made the running:

"So you are.....Umbulala?!!"

A bottomless hush followed, when not even the wind bestirred its wings. Umbulala caught his breath, and his thoughts raced:

"He....he knows my name - but how??!"

As if reading the cub's mind, the big cat proceeded to enlighten him:

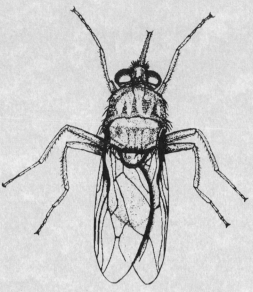

"Many moons have come and gone - indeed, more full moons than my forepaws have claws - since that long night, high on the escarpment, when I lay on guard as your mother gave birth to three cubs......"

Umbulala felt frozen onto the branch, an unfamiliar ache quivering and rising in his gullet as the stranger continued,

".......one, I was later to learn, as dark as night's star-crested hollow: one that the eagle owl told me Brother wind had predicted would be the greatest of all the jungle's hunters, and thus the most feared of Mother nature's cats. So I have returned, but briefly, to see for myself this singular cub of such promise which I, Bulala, have sired......."

His heart thumping like a bullfrog demented, understanding screamed in Umbulala's head as the stranger's meaning poured towards him:

"and to give that cub the benefit of a father's long seasons in the jungle."

The gulf between them at once melted away - though neither cat moved a whisker's breadth. For what seemed an eternity of seasons they continued to stare in each other's direction. The older cat was well in command, but his brooding, sulphureous eyes bore the cub no threat. Umbulala remained transfixed on his scaly perch, so run through was he with feelings he couldn't fully grasp, as never was there a cub more privileged for such an experience.

"And a great hunter you may some moons hence become......"

Bulala continued,

"as so predicted by that fleet whispering spirit of the air, Brother wind. But mark well little panther! Hunt not the hairless ape; nor that which dwells in its den. Here is a hunter of another kind; a hunter that, if it should but glimpse you in that shining coat of night, will not rest until it has taken the very skin from your back, leaving your naked carcass for the dogs to snigger over, and the jackals and hyaenas to gorge themselves on.

"Beware the hairless apes, Umbulala - the ones that walk straight and upright like the heron. From far away, sometimes too far to be seen, they will spit like the cobra - so hard and so strong it will knock you over. Your insides will burn as though seared by fire, and your blood will spout hot rivers from your body as you reel in the clutches of death's savage hold; and all the while the hairless ones will stand watching you, right through to your last dragging constrictions! What hairless ape administers is something far removed from the quick painless end we leopards render our prey."

Bulala rose, extending one hind leg. It looked as if it had been savagely bitten at one time or another. Now healed, a chunk of flesh the size of a marula fruit was missing from the fleshy part of the thigh.

"Here is but a small sample of their work!"

Bulala motioned to the old wound.

"The hairless ones don't hunt to eat as we do. They will behead a fine antelope or buffalo, and leave the body behind to be mocked and slavered over by the scavengers! Often they will take only the back legs and leave the rest. Not even the giants of the jungle, the mighty

elephant and rhinoceros, are safe from their vile ways. Like the antlion, the hairless ones lay secret traps under the sand for the unsuspecting, covered over with leaves. Some will spear you, or leave you dangling ignominiously from a tree by the neck, or a leg, so to strangle you.......or condemn you to death by slow starvation.

"Sometimes they will trick you with a tempting piece of meat that has been tethered to a root, or just left to lay on the ground. Now, some might say that dead flesh is worth finding: it saves risking your life hunting down your prey and killing it! On the contrary. Meat bespoiled by the hairless one will rip and tear at your insides, and make your body quake in violent fits that bend you double from head to tail, while you retch and writhe in pain; wracked by a raging thirst and drained of every strength. You may die, or you may live....at the expense of being the weakest you'll ever be throughout all your seasons in the jungle, and thus the most vulnerable to attack by hyaena, lion, baboon; losing half your weight or more, much of your fur in patches, and gaining a bitter taste for all to do with the hairless ones.

"So Umbulala! Should Brother wind bring you but a whiff of the hairless ones, neither walk in their tread, nor be enticed by their tainted food. The hairless ones care not if they catch in their traps, cat or antelope, young or old. Many is the jungle creature I have seen dying the slow death wrought by their savage snares and pitfalls: the worst by far the elephant. Wasting away little by little because it could no longer eat or drink enough to survive, its trunk, its lifeline, had been severed by a hard, sharp, snake-like thing that looked for all the world like a vine hanging in a tree, cunningly disguised by the leaves and branches the elephant feeds on.

"One mighty bull I saw had been dragging around behind him for moons too numerous, a large log that had caught around one of his hind legs by means of a long, noisy, twisted vine that glistens, and can't
be broken. The poor giant couldn't shake it off. As he moved about, it cut deeper and deeper into the leg with the pull and drag of the log, until eventually the foot rotted. Thus, while the maggots had their fill, the great elephant hobbled on from sunrise to sunset, dying bit by bit with the pain and the racing decay in his leg, which gradually sickened through his whole body.

"Not even the elephant's tusks are sacred; nor the strange horn of that short-tempered rogue the rhino, which is not horn - as the antelopes have - but a cone of tightly woven hair perched atop its snout. Even these the hairless apes take, and what's harder to understand, a foot or a tail which they flail the air with, wrap around them.......or sit on! Oh, strange indeed are the hairless ones. Why, it seems that what they fear above all else is the tiny insects of the jungle - tsetse flies and fever mosquitoes - from which they flee, frantically pawing and scratching themselves as they go!!

"Yes, strange indeed are the hairless ones. Remember too, Umbulala - hairless ape kills hairless ape. But not to eat; nor even to take each other's skin like they do ours. No. When the hairless ones kill each other.......the hyaena is the only taker! So beware Umbulala, for there is little justice in the death they deal out so freely. Your mother will have taught you well, for her skill and courage are renowned across jungle tract and beyond. But of the hairless ones she knows little, and fortunate it is too. Tell her I was here."

And with that, like a mottled wraith, Bulala breezed away, leaving only a hush of jungle to mark his wake. Umbulala made no attempt to follow. He knew better than to do that.

He pondered awhile on the mysteries Bulala had revealed to him, dreamily wondering, as any right-minded cub would in the circumstances, if and when the day would ever come when he would be likened to such a magnificent master hunter! Sighing wistfully, he clawed distractedly at the branch he was lying along, before turning to nose a leaf. In craving perfection he instinctively took one step closer to attaining it.

Ingwe was philosophical about the news when Umbulala burst out with it the moment he saw her. In truth, it had taken her somewhat by surprise as she had just been about to warn the cub that Bulala was in the area, having come across his scent down by the river. Her concern was not unfounded -

predators of Bulala's eminence don't take kindly to cubs, whatever their breeding! In the delicately balanced structure of nature, the established leopard views any up-and-coming young cat as just one more competitor for territory and game it will endeavour to annihilate at the first opportunity. Ingwe looked upon Umbulala's unique experience as a positive triumph for the one lesson of life that is the hardest to learn: its unpredictability.

"You are indeed blessed little one!"

she remarked on hearing Umbulala's startling account of his meeting with his father.

"He has much wisdom wrought of long experience. Hearken to that advice, and hold it close to your heart. In the seasons that lay ahead, it could well mark your deliverance."

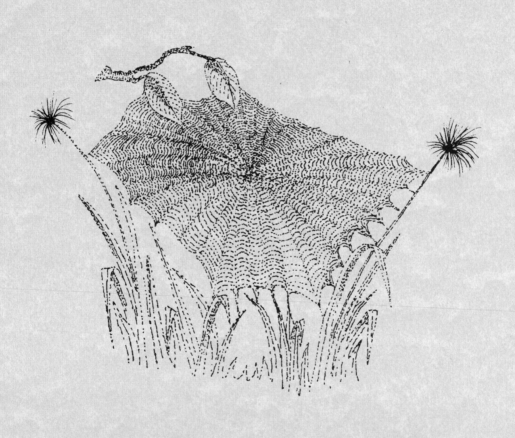

NOSE TO THE WIND

Listen to the reeds ....
they have a song to sing

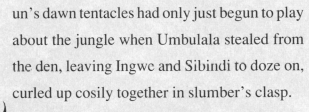

un's dawn tentacles had only just begun to play about the jungle when Umbulala stealed from the den, leaving Ingwe and Sibindi to doze on, curled up cosily together in slumber's clasp.

"Ah, to be on the hunt again!",

his thoughts sang as he slipped quietly away between caressing ferns splattered with the filmy damp of early morning, the air fragrant with the crisp feel of the dry season.

Licking a tongue-cup of dew from a leaf to tingle awake his senses, Umbulala gazed up at the ascending sun, a splendid vermilion orb now cradling the escarpment from end to end in a ripening ripple of morning's first blush. He dropped down over the glow-washed shoulder of rock to the bottom of the escarpment. Here, the hazy, pre-dawn traces still hung heavy in mist. Even the trees and shrubs plotted ghostly shapes in the shimmering chrysalis of daybreak; while generously festooning the here and theres, silver-spangled spider webs, glistening with myriad dewdrops, diffused their glitter through the eerie half-light.

Umbulala's saturated senses drank in the phantasmagoria before him - the ethereal morning world of the wilds! Only dawn's chorusing ranks of birdsong, welcoming harbinger of the new day, dispelled any feeling of otherworldliness. Everywhere hung nets of spidery abode. One enormous web, made up of a multiplicity of fine strands as taut as cats whiskers, spanned a good, full-grown leopard's length between two trees. And while Umbulala noted that the resident spider wasn't in, there was certainly no shortage of callers! This spurious gossamer was so strong, it was able to catch and hold on its sticky hairs-breadth fibres the largest of moths and butterflies - like magnificent moon moths and swallowtails. Even small birds weren't immune, and would hang helpless till an injection of the spider's deadly serum brought an end to their struggle.

"Mother nature hasn't given spiders much in life........"

Umbulala chuckled to himself,

"but what she has, they make the most of! Why, if a spider was as large as me........"

his thoughts took a sober turn,

"it could well catch an......an.....*elephant*!"

And the idea of such a thing horrified him.

"Yes indeed!"

He nodded to himself reassuringly.

"Mother Nature is definitely *wise* in making spiders small!"

Turning to go on his way, he shot one last glance at the spider's web by way of making certain that everything was just as it had been the last time he'd looked - its many dewy cross-threads of transparency twinkling like kaleidoscopes of sunrise in dawn's light.

Umbulala wandered on. Done with sight-seeing for the moment, he turned his attention to the more serious task of keeping an eagle eye out for a good vantage point from where to lay an ambush. He was no longer the little cumbersome cub of old, with pincushion paws, always at

Ingwe's heels. A lusty young cat, well into the second dry season of his days, he had matured well; certainly faster and more completely than Sibindi who, though adept in her skills, was inclined to be somewhat over-hasty for her own good.

Apart from male leopards being larger of build than their female counterparts, Umbulala was a big cat; bigger than what was customary. This, and a steady, open approach to life - which owed as much to his own receptiveness, as it did to Ingwe's teaching - is of untold significance in the growing process. The time was rapidly approaching when he would make that final break with cubhood by leaving the den to go off on his own; taking as his one talisman, and most valued asset, the knowledge imparted in wisdom and affection down all those cubhood days.

Where a large tree, struck by lightning at some stage previous, had taken a lunge across a game trail, right into the outstretched arms of another tree on the opposite flank, an arch had formed above the path, thereby presenting a perfect promontory on which to perch and lie in wait for any unwary animal that might happen to stroll under. And while being cool and comfortable of outlook, it presented the panther with a precious opportunity to muse, undisturbed, on the nuances of nature, while attending to those banal demands life makes in the matter of grooming and keeping claws up to scratch.

Umbulala nestled in, watching with delight the early rays of sunlight winking through the interlaced foliage above him, weaving, with every wisp of breeze, delicate designs on the ground below - shadowy patterns that skipped back and forth like flocks of black butterflies flitting from flower to flower. It put Umbulala in mind of the lesson of Brother wind. Consort of the clouds, harbinger of rain, or simple balm in the scorching clutch of midday, the wind is a most valued bringer of news via the scents and smells of the jungle - from blossoms, dung and dry grass, rotting vegetation, the

tang of rain settling the dust after
noontide, to the very animals
themselves, bearing odours distinct
to each.

And over the seasons of time,
jungle creatures have evolved a
way of reading the merest
impressions of scent, or sound,
carried on the wind as a means of
heeding the approach of food, friend or foe. Umbulala remembered Ingwe
telling him of Mother nature's prediction when she bestowed this unique and
wonderful gift on the animals:

"Use it wisely, and it will serve you well",
she had urged.

"Disregard it, and I will reclaim it from your kind forever."
He at once recalled the hairless apes Bulala had warned him about. He had
heard from the eagle owl that only once did Mother nature have recourse to
her threat, and that was when she withdrew the gift from the hairless ones
for choosing to scorn it:

"Foolish creatures!" he sniffed contemptuously.
Umbulala's sensitive nostrils twitched as he tested the breeze - but it only
seemed to whisper back through the interminable maze of leaves and
branches: *nothing for you yet little brotherrrrrr*.

Time ticked imperceptibly by. Even the brilliant yellow weaver bird nearby
had lost all interest in Umbulala, now more akin to a bronze effigy, so
motionless was the black cat on the overhang of the deformed tree. Besotted
with weaving the finest nest around for a future mate, his little masked head
nodded tirelessly as he carried on an argument with a colourful pair of red
bishop birds. Their scarlet plumes, aflame in the sunlight, contrasted vividly
with their little, glossy black chests that were puffed up in disgust at the

goings-on of the lovesick weaver, who never once seemed to cease his toil, or incessant chatter. Somewhere a turtledove gently called. And Umbulala thought how like a soft purr it sounded in contrast to the infernal prattle of the weaver and his pompous neighbours - mellow and soothing as a heartbeat! And brother wind sighed through the jungle in seeming agreement.

Umbulala lifted his head, scenting a message on the breeze.

"Hmmm.....rhino somewhere."

The cat shrugged it off in the same breath. Not quite the sport for leopard; not unless he wanted to be irretrievably chomped into cat chow! The scent of something else followed; something a little more to his taste. Lifting his top lip, Umbulala exposed his scent glands full into the breeze, to make the most of what he'd nosed riding so faintly on the back of brother wind.

"Wildebeest......some way off, beyond the rhino - with buffalo trailing." The panther grunted to himself:

"A tender calf would do just fine."

Flexing his claws and licking his lips in anticipation, he murmured pleasurably at the thought. His mind wandered to the time his mother advised him never to tangle with buffalo when he was grown up, unless it was a very young calf at a distance back from the herd, and only a few leaps from him so to make a successful attack feasible. Buffalo are fearless fighters and more than respected for it. Moreover; to be gored to death by one of the thundering oafs certainly wasn't to his liking! Hence he must judge any situation involving buffalo with the utmost caution, retreating if necessary.

Many is the attack on buffalo that has been turned completely around, with the buffalo's would-be killer ending up the victim, and usually to its eternal woe. Of all the jungle predators lion are perhaps their most consistent foe; leopards being generally too light to tempt fate to such an extent. But great opportunists as leopards are, there have been occasions where a cunning, quick-thinking leopard has taken advantage of unusual circumstances to successfully overcome a calf. These are exceptions to the rule, and uncommon at that. Yet when they occur, they are the talk of the jungle for seasons too numerous to recount.

"Wildebeest have sheered off; rhino too!" Umbulala noted, his fine scenting ability picking up the change of direction. A knot began to form in his stomach as the most intense feeling of excitement gripped him. Arrayed along a rise - probably some twenty elephant lengths upwind of him - was the buffalo herd, a good thirty or more strong, and looking to be everywhere at once!

At first glance they appeared as not much more than hazy ant-hills in among the cover of trees and scrub that lay between. Only a flicker of sunlight off a massive, bossed horn told otherwise - monstrous weapons Umbulala had heard buffalo were extremely adept at using to their fullest potential. There was nothing those horns couldn't disembowel! Even the buffalo's hooves, like slate-edged granite chunks, could make minced meat of a flagging cat any day. Ingwe had once shown Umbulala the remains of one unfortunate lion that had been systematically chopped into oblivion by a bull buffalo, before being ground into the earth until the carcass was barely recognisable. By way of finishing matters off, the bull had rolled over and over its victim until satisfied it was never getting up again!

With such thoughts running rampant in his mind, Umbulala was more than relieved the herd had halted some distance upwind of him, doubtless to let the slow ones catch up. He had heard their sense of smell bettered, in some instances, even that of the cats - and suddenly Umbulala seriously began to question his sanity in not

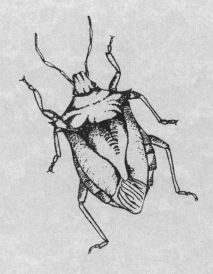

having already got out of that tree and away. So few weak points have buffalo, combined with a stunning aggregate of assets such as the most powerful set of horns around, sheer brute strength and a courage to match, that the animal seems virtually indestructible. Even their hearing is exceptional.

But nothing in life is so indestructible that fate doesn't leave a chink for the wise and wily to find. As Umbulala eyed the herd from atop his vantage point high above the game trail, it struck him how much like thick tree trunks the necks of buffalo were. And that strange hunched look they seemed to affect: was it due to the weight of the horns, or perhaps their downward sweep which, when buffalo stick their large black noses into the wind, gives them such a supercilious, calculating mien; almost like you owed them something! Suddenly the panther had no more time for puzzles. The whole herd was converging his way.

Ponderously, methodically, massed hooves struck the ground like flintstones, building to thunder pitch amid the bawls and moos of the steadily approaching throng. Closer and closer they rumbled down towards the arch - a rolling battalion of force that sent vibrations shivering and pulsing along the ground, and up the trees, so constituting the jungle's very own grapevine telegraph which animals are so expert at deciphering. Soon the front guard was within but a few paces of the arch, and for the first time Umbulala got a clear view of the herd. Calves, if any, would be scattered throughout it, mainly from the centre backwards. From his leafy hide Umbulala peered down with the sharp eyes of the predator about to strike. The drumming of hooves rose to a thunder, shaking up a storm that reached on up to the veil of branches and foliage concealing the cat.

Umbulala stiffened, a barb of concentration. Through the irritant pall of dust thrown up as the throng passed directly beneath him, his keen eyes picked out a tender young calf, plodding along at the back of the herd. Umbulala acted swiftly. With the entire herd now all but through the arch, speed was paramount. Doing a quick about-face, he checked for a rearguard.

The coast was clear. In another instant the lagging calf would be right in range.

Umbulala arched his body like an unsprung bow - a heartbeat later he was in the air and landing on the calf's rump, knocking it over in one deft movement. The calf turned its head in mute surprise toward its assailant, just as Umbulala dealt it a deathblow in one crushing bite to the throat. The effort it takes a leopard to pounce, overpower and kill its prey can constitute an expulsion of energy which can very nearly exhaust it. The panther lay a moment without moving, still ahold of the calf's neck, sucking the salty blood that is such a revitalizer in the bid to regain strength quickly.

But chance wasn't going to allow much time for that. The instant Umbulala pounced on the tiring calf, the herd was alerted. The wind now in their favour, no longer the panther's, a phalanx of horned, hard-nosed faces wheeled round in his direction. They had missed the actual kill, but the buffalo at the rear of the herd sighted the motionless calf immediately. With that innate, uncanny sense mothers have of knowing their own, an old cow extricated herself from out of a line of horns. Burning eyes riveted on the spot where the carcass lay. Rolling forward like a ton boulder down a mountain slope, the cow galumphed into motion, pumping enough adrenalin for two. Hammer-head hooves pelted the ground as she snorted and bellowed, her huge leathered nostrils blowing enough steam to match the dust she'd churned up, vengeance her only spur. Those inexorable forces with which nature holds life to ransom were moving into play.

Umbulala was a creative cat. And it was this attribute in such a tight situation that was to prove his redemption. Crouching low, as if making ready to pounce - as all cats instinctively do when threatened - the panther noticed that the black of his coat melded completely with the shadow between the legs of the calf cast by the early morning sun. Better cover he couldn't have hoped for in the circumstances, given that the old cow looked bent on carrying through her charge!

With all the fury of a fireball she was bearing down on the carcass even as Umbulala watched, hidden in the shadowed hollow of the dead calf's legs. Her scarred flanks spoke of glories over lion left as carrion long ago. Merciless, searching eyes seemed to be scrutinizing every hair's-breadth of space in the vicinity of the carcass; the cow's colossal hooked horns sweeping the air like battering rams. She drew adjacent, and the odour of leopard filled her nostrils. An enraged cry cut the air as eyes, in anguished, searching glances, sought the spotted cur that had slain her calf: the leopard she wouldn't have expected to be anything but spotted. But the cow found only the blood-smeared carcass of the motionless calf, her last. She was too old to give birth again.

"Oh, *why* did he not take me?!"

she groaned, the greyness around her neck and face, the hairless patches on her hide, attesting to great age.

"It was long ago I was so young. Instead, the old are left to contend a tortuous and tormented end, torn apart by the wild dog pack!! Not for us the quick and painless death.....!"

Flinging her head back, the old cow buffalo scoured the treetops with blazing eyes, as though looking for an answer from Mother nature. The calf was dead. In lingering she threatened her own existence, and in this the jungle gives no quarter. Her eyes were bloodshot. Rage clouded them; she did not notice the panther lying there between the dead calf's stomach and hind legs in the deep, burrowing shadow thrown by the sun. Never had she encountered a black leopard; never would she have looked for one.

Umbulala wasn't foolish to believe fortune would smile on him much longer. He was sure the old cow's lapse of sight was but a temporary thing; wrought of a miasma of emotion uncompromisingly destructive in a world where Brother error curries no favours. The facts of the situation were coldly simple - kill or be killed. The moment the buffalo had dropped her guard by raising her head and exposing her neck, its skin now gaunt and sagged with age, Umbulala had seen his chance; an odds on chance that comes but once. The cat reasoned that if he was going to risk being killed, it was clearly better at these odds to fight his way out, with a chance of surviving, than to just give in to the mind-numbing prospect of being pounded to death by buffalo!

Slicker than thought, the panther struck. Grappling-iron jaws grasped the buffalo's throat at its most vulnerable point just below the jaw, where the skin was relatively soft and somewhat time-worn, sinking sickle-sharp teeth down to the windpipe to crush the very breath out of his formidable adversary. Time blurred, as with long, spiked fangs striking deep, he wrenched and squeezed and hung on with all the ferocity and tenacity of his kind. The cow reeled backwards, not entirely certain what had hit her; just a sweetly numb sensation coursing through her, disarming her senses.

"Oh hunter of the shadows!"

she gasped, her windpipe ripped and all but disgorged of life,

"your bite is the sting of death - yet I bear you no malice. The touch of Mother nature is balm enough."

Like the slow motion birth of a landslip, her sturdy cabriole legs crumpled, and she sank to the ground, life fast ebbing away. With his flanks heaving, Umbulala never let go his grip; not for a heartbeat. Moments later she was dead. The herd, watching from a distance off, began to reassemble......then

solemnly trundled away. They'd witnessed two kinds of courage this day -
one how to die, the other how to live.

Ingwe and Sibindi were high up on the escarpment, shaking off sleep, when
they heard it: the low, plaintive, and unmistakable wail of dying buffalo
sighing through the jungle, setting slips of grass and weed to hobnob with
the sheer moment of it. From beneath the patchwork of treetops below the
rocky ramparts out front of the den, to where they'd hastily scurried, it drifted
up: a mournful, soul-searching lament that echoed along the escarpment, then
died.

Suddenly another distinctive cry floated across the dulled reaches, and over
the jungle canopy on the back of Brother wind. It was the sawing cough of
leopard; a familiar call mother and sister recognised as Umbulala's, inviting
them to come and share a trophy too big for one alone to devour, or drag up
a tree to make safe from scavengers.

News of the event spread like fire through drywood. Even as the three
began to eat their fill, consuming first the heart, liver and remaining viscera
from both carcasses - Umbulala having already buried the distasteful
entrails out of the way of scavengers - a flurry of vultures with drooping,
bald heads were already gathering in the overhanging trees, each rapacious
and itching to be in the feast.

Hung back out of sight amid the shadowed undergrowth a single hyaena
and three jackal lurked, reverent and fawning, patiently biding their time -
the awe of the moment still ringing through the wild jungle morning. And
henceforward it was to remain for Umbulala wherever along nature's ways
destiny was to take him.

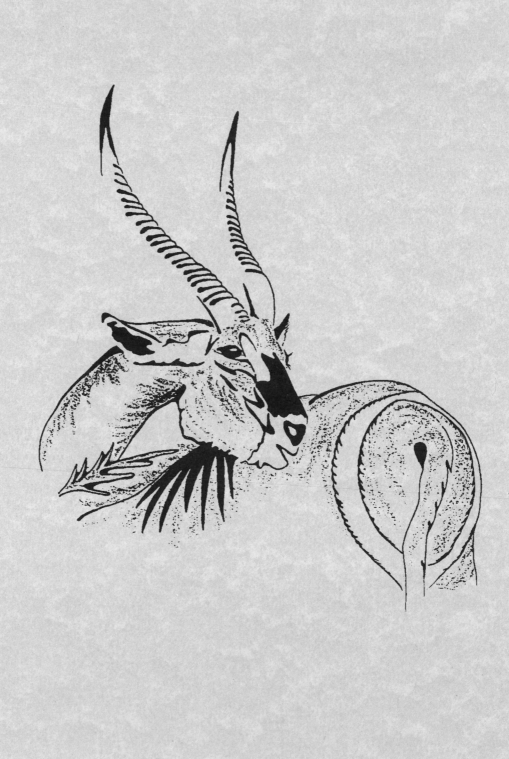

THE PRECIPICE

*Tomorrow's cloak of gossamer
is already unfolding*

uch was made in jungle circles of Umbulala's daring and unprecedented repulse of the buffalo. Indeed, the entire family had taken a respite from hunting as a result; the two carcasses proving more than enough food for the three of them.

"There is really no point in hunting purely for the sake of it...."

Ingwe had remarked to Umbulala and Sibindi one afternoon some time later, as they strolled together along the crest of the escarpment.

"When we do, we put our lives at risk every time."

Sauntering along in the bold, prismatic sunshine that is such a feature of tropical reaches, their sumptuous coats shone, each cat visibly glowing with good health and élan! Here, on the upper reaches of the escarpment, and in and around its secretive ledges and crevices, was one of the few areas where the leopards could relax with any degree of ease. What's more, from atop the boulders ringing its upper ramparts, they could see right across the jungle. And on a clear day it constituted a veritable feast for the eyes!

Across a frothy swathe of green that ran the gamut of vegetal tones, river traces and game paths cut serpentine trails. Dotted in between - some with pools or mudholes harbouring an array of wallowers from hippopotamus to

warthog - clean, chlorine clearings, cropped to a fine sward, crept with ant-like herds of wildebeest and impala and zebra.

Umbulala decided to go on ahead, leaving his mother and sister to amble on together along a lower ledge. He leapt with ease to a parallel shelf a good few bounds further up the rock. Without losing sight, or sense, of them, he began playing at camouflage, darting moth-like from shadow to shadow. The world seemed thoroughly at peace, an atmosphere of melodious quiet pervading it in a way only the wild can so completely encapsulate.

It continued to appear so, right up to the instant the air unexpectedly erupted in an ear-wringing stridor of animal sounds.   An urgent rush, somewhere further down the escarpment's precipitous slope, was all that preceded it; moments later, without warning, it broke into a chilling cacophony of barks and shrieks that WAUGHED! and BOOMED! into every hollow and cranny of rock, riveting Umbulala to the spot! Way below him, like marauding rats whooping it up and barking hysterically in the dramatic way of their kind, a troop of baboons was swarming over the scarp face toward Ingwe and Sibindi. Of the anonymous figure lying watching with sedulous concern from the shadowed crevices above, they seemed completely unaware.

Already Ingwe and Sibindi's path along the rock ledge had been blocked across the front and rear by dog baboons from the troops vanguard; dagger-like canines attesting to formidable combat capabilities. On a ledge above, amid an attendant crowd of retainers jeering down at the cornered pair, squatted the troop leader, the dominant dog baboon in vulturish mood:

"Kosi the lion will have a real feast......"
he scoffed loudly,

"and he won't even have to hunt it down!"

Whoops of derision arose from the baboon throng.

"Why, when we force the two of you off the edge, you'll plunge to a death you well deserve - and not a drop of blood will my kind or I have shed!"

With a triumphant cry the dog rallied the troop:

"Come baboons, arm yourselves with stones and we'll show this bitch leopard and her overgrown cub!!"

The prospect of ridding the jungle of two leopards, the dreaded enemy, in one swoop was too much for the baboons! So worked up with bloodlust did they become, all thought of troop defences disintegrated in a moment, like rain upon a glassy shore. A moment was enough. In times of tense activity, baboons generally keep to a strict hierarchical formation. Pregnant females and those carrying young at the heart of the throng are ringed by dominant dogs, which are surrounded in turn by subordinate females and adolescents. Sentinels are posted strategically around the perimeter, and dominant dogs bring up the rear. Such a stratagem forgotten could, on occasion, have merciless repercussions.

Umbulala crouched, flat as lichen on a rock. He carefully checked the wind, finding where it favoured him best. Then, like a shadow, he edged closer to the core of baboons, their leader at the centre, grouped precariously on the escarpment edge, and still leering down at the cornered leopards. Sniggering and jeering with every stone hurled at the cats, the baboons jostled and pushed one another to peer down and bark scornfully at Ingwe and Sibindi, helplessly trapped on the rock ledge below. Suddenly, above the clamour, a full-throated roar rose firm and clear from Ingwe:

"RUN...RUN..UMBULALA! RUN!"

Until now the task of attack had looked dicey, if not downright dangerous to the panther. But when the old dog baboon who led the troop yelled back, blind with scorn:

"HA! There's none but you two - Kosi killed your other cub....!"
Umbulala's ice control snapped. At the very mention of the accursed Kosi
who had slain his sister Kusasa the season before, the panther, in a buffeting
expulsion of power and fury, rose from the shadows behind them like the
spectre of death. With a terrifying, piercing roar that sawed the atmosphere
through, hacking across the stormy hubbub like a thunderclap, the panther
launched headlong into the attack. Those he loved best in all the jungle stood
in peril of their lives.

Leopard, with skill and intelligence unadorned by manufacture, is not
designed to cower in fear. That moment of decision, that irrevocable moment
he chose to charge the baboons - still unwittingly turned away from him -
Umbulala came of age. He leapt through the air in an exploding arabesque
of fury. Falling on the dominant dog in virtually the same moment, Umbulala
wrenched it backwards with scalpelled claws hooked around the victim's
throat. The panther sunk his teeth deep into the nape of its neck, severing
the baboon's spinal cord with one savage twist of an ebony head, before
releasing his grip to let the body fall onto the ledge below in front of the
baboons blocking his mother and sister's path. Before the troop had time to
grasp what was happening, Umbulala had split open the rib cage of the next
startled baboon, its blood gushing out in torrents with every pumping beat
of its quaking heart.

A leopard at the height of a charge from close quarters, hurtling through
the air at blinding speed, is little more than
a spine-chilling blur to the unfortunate at
the wrong end of its fury. The sight of the
carnage set Ingwe's mind racing. With a
screaming roar that left none in doubt of
her intention, she pitched headfirst into the
huddle of distracted baboons blocking the
rear. One by one they fell in a frenzied

bloodbath of skulls smashed, and throats torn asunder. It was an uphill fight; but the older leopardess was imbued with a lust to kill, and she gave no quarter.

The younger female was of the same temper. Taking advantage of first Umbulala's diversion, then Ingwe's full frontal assault on the rearguard, Sibindi hurled herself at the nearest baboon, one of four blocking the front. In the flick of a swallow's wing, she had crushed its skull like it was eggshell, tossing the twitching carcass over the precipice. The others lost their footing in the panic, tottering off the ledge to their death, fearful screams marking the traces of their fall. With the way in front of her now clear, Sibindi streaked round the last boulder, and up onto the furthermost ledge where her brother was - now well deep in battle.

The spot she came up on offered an advantageous position from which to angle an attack. It also served the baboon troop with the only means of escape off the ledge - and Sibindi couldn't help thinking what a grand place it would be in a last stand! In the face of so many baboons, a last stand was what it might well be. But the troop appeared confused and in disarray. A sense of mob panic appeared to be taking hold. Recognising this, Sibindi cried out a challenge to the baboons, hoping to confuse those around Umbulala, and thereby relieve the pressure on him:

"I, Sibindi, will not let one of you treacherous, grinning monkeys pass alive!!"

As if her cry had been a command to do just that, a wave of baboons turned en masse - and descended in her direction so to secure a way through by sheer force of numbers with little blood loss. But psychologically the tide of battle had turned against them. Sibindi came into her own. For those baboons that didn't slip and fall in the rush, plummeting headlong off the escarpment, the implacable spotted cat stood before them like a sprung dynamo, goring and ripping with all the skill only those of the leopard temperament inherit.

Soon the entire area, on and below the escarpment, lay bloated with carcasses; some agonised in the last-gasp throes of life, most, with a mere twitch of muscle, paid deference to death. Those that hadn't fallen off the precipice just staggered about. While a few choked, or clutched their wounds - a jugular vein foaming and bloodied from a mortal swipe of a dew claw, a scalp cleaved clean open - others, disembowelled and gagging with pain and fear, were stuffing spilled entrails back into the gapping hole where their guts had once been, vainly trying to hold it altogether with clumps of grass. Elsewhere among the throng, moribund unfortunates wandered like zombies, coughing up clots of blood blighted with bile.

Mindful not to let her guard slip in the brief lull that followed, Sibindi advanced with stealth towards Umbulala - engaged in dealing with what remained of the troop - just as Ingwe rounded up behind him. Together, the two females had in effect executed a perfect buffalo horn attack. With the panther launching an all-out assault on the very core of the troop, attention had been diverted long enough from Ingwe and Sibindi for the leopardess pair to break through the ambush, and fight back.

There stood the panther, weary-worn and dripping with the bloody disgorge of battle - dead and wounded baboons arraigned stricken and prostrate about him. Out of a thirty strong troop that undertook the attack, less than half a dozen survived, and that was only after a death-defying leap to another ledge; a leap that for many proved fatal. Most either lost their footing on takeoff, or missed the ledge altogether. Others had already fallen to their deaths out of sheer fright, thereby foregoing the unenviable task of facing the wrathful might of the panther, his mother and his sister.

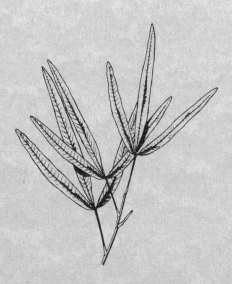

The family drank their fill of blood, and then lay up in the shade awhile; later returning to the den to sleep off the day in unimpeachable triumph. Scores of vultures had already gathered in the heavens, languorously scrolling lazy circles on eddying downdrafts of thermals. Only when the leopards took their leave would they venture to land.

The sight of so many vultures circling in the sky in one place pointed to a kill, thus attracting considerable attention; not in the least from Kosi. Because of his crippled mouth, hunting was a chore. Thus, ready-made kills were a boon. But others, too, had seen the circling vultures. And by the time Kosi had arrived at the scene on the escarpment, the area was crowded: crowded out with animals gazing in stunned appraisal of the devastation around them! Clinging to a ledge just a little way from the lion were the jibbering and trembling survivors; a forlorn little group huddled against the gnarled and battered rock face. It made for a pathetic sight. But from Kosi, so preoccupied with his own problems, sympathy was about as unexpected as it is from a bont tick.

"What attacked your troop?...."

he shouted across at them over the heads of a bevy of jackals and vultures; coldly indifferent as he blandly licked the fur off the stomach of one carcass, before opening it up to eat. A decidedly shaken old bitch baboon, most senior of the group, replied hesitantly, her eyes fixed and anxious:

"T'was a black leopard, and two others......spotted! A monstrous black cat, the likes of which I have never seen throughout all my seasons in the jungle! He struck like Brother lightning from out of nowhere, and none stood in his way. Why, at one point I saw almost as many dogs as a baboon has fingers, some amongst the troop's largest and bravest, attack him simultaneously. Yet in a wink of an owl's eyelid, all were left dead, or dying....!"

Suddenly she broke off, turning in feverish haste to the other survivors with the urgent plea:

> "Come, let's away! I cannot bear to see these scavengers fill themselves on our kin."

Checking the path ahead, the haunted little band moved off along the ledge, nervous, and sore of spirit and body. Kosi shrugged and ate on.

> "One things for sure!"

he chuckled,

> "that fat black cub of Ingwe's has certainly provided a fine meal!"

An imposing voice suddenly sounded across the castellated face of the escarpment, so startling Kosi he very nearly choked.

> "That fat black cub of which you so scornfully speak, lion that is but half a lion, is no fat cub - but a grown leopard, well beyond the usual size for its kind, and of such fearsome propensity and skill, I fear it will be sick lion that jungle scavengers will some day soon be feeding on!"

Kosi spun round, full of characteristic bluster and indignation, ready to take to task the upstart who'd dare intimate such a thing; bits of carrion hanging limp and scurrilous from his crippled mouth. Pruning the amber tinted feathers down its neck, a chic bateleur eagle, perched in a crevice above Kosi, swivelled its handsome head around to peer down imperiously at the lion:

> "Enjoy it Kosi...."

it barked a command,

> "as from what my eyes witnessed of this fight, your days are numbered!"

Visibly shaken by the bateleur's warning, Kosi stared back openmouthed at the colourful eagle - one of an elegant, stub-tailed breed renowned throughout the jungle for its soaring flight and masterful tumbling abilities. The noble cast and large head atop a broad, black chest gives the bateleur such an imposing air of omniscience, the lion didn't press for an explanation; preferring instead blissful ignorance to knowing the worst. But he caught its warning - and for the first time in all his born days an unusual fear slithered like an icy ripple through his body, chastening his very bones with its dire sense of foreboding.

🐾   🐾   🐾

Ingwe watched Umbulala as he lay sleeping, and mused wistfully. His killing of the buffalo was already legendary; and of this latest feat? She hardly needed wonder. Now more than ever she was certain the time had come, and the awareness of it hung heavy on her heart. The panther's eyes opened and looked directly at her: cold and slanted of gaze, they at once clouded with affection, seeming to read her very thoughts.

"You look troubled mother..?"

he ventured questioningly,

"as though you have something to say yet can't find the heart. I never thought I would ever see the day when you would falter - even if only in giving wing to your thoughts!"

Ingwe sighed.

"I feel you may well have guessed them already; just as I feel you know you are ready to leave and seek out hunting grounds of your own. When you do find that territory Umbulala, guard it well and drink of its wonders. But remember......"

she intoned fervently,

"yesterday the three of us pledged our lives to one another. Never lose that memory Umbulala."

Like-mind, like-spirit, like-whole - a very part of her was leaving, and her meaning did little to disguise it. Ambling over to him, she rubbed her spotted head against his, now already bigger than hers. Umbulala rolled over, playfully feigning an attack on his sister still curled up in sleep. Turning back to Ingwe, he remarked matter-of-factly, his mood solemn:

"Mother, I leave here today, but no territory shall I mark out till I've avenged the death of Kusasa........"

the warmth fled from his eyes, as they coloured with the usual, chill resolve of leopard,

"and the time has come for that!" By the next full moon you will know that I have killed Kosi the sick lion - or he has killed me!"

With Umbulala, her eldest born, the leopardess always felt that he listened to her; or at least respected her advice. So she offered him a warning that was by way of being her one last lesson to her cub before that irrevocable, predestined parting:

"Umbulala, ill as Kosi is, he is brave.....and deadly. Shed of all his fat, what remains is a body of pure muscle. Above all, he is imbued with the will to live. Tread carefully little one. Grant that Mother nature will favour you with the art and strength to rid the jungle of this troublesome beast, and thenceforth guide you safely along its ways."

Umbulala tipped his head up, cat-like in acknowledgement, and for a fleeting moment gazed deep into his mother's soulful eyes. Then, without so much as a backward glance, he left the den, and cubhood, behind forever.

BOTH SIDES OF THE LEAF

*A fly is a jewel to Mother nature
..........and a feast for a frog!*

As the wise watcher in the woods well knows, there is always something to learn from nature; that although cubhood may pass like a melodious caprice that gets dimmer with the memory, the learning goes on. Perched on a granite boulder, or striking a more soigné pose high up in a tree, Umbulala could squat endlessly without regard to time's trenchant tug, just observing the intricate curiosities of his jungle world - thrilling as much at the sight of a sleek, tuft-eared caracal catching a bird on the wing, as at a butterfly alighting on a blossom.

It is said that there's nothing new under the sun. But for this willing initiate everything was new, and already his senses had benefited double- fold. Even his stalking technique had honed to an exactness his colour ably abetted, especially in the rocky and shady traces he favoured. Passing within a few bounds of a thicket one morning, he was brought up short by an urgent snort crosswind of him. It sounded like the alarm call of some large antelope; exactly what type he wasn't sure. His felid curiosity got the better of him.

Nearby was a heavily gnarled, granite outcrop flanking the thicket. It also directly overlooked it, and would make an ideal prominence. With caution his mentor, Umbulala slinked stealthily toward it, careful all the while to keep himself downwind of the object of his interest. Creeping right up onto the kopje, he gingerly climbed it; springing lastly to a rock higher up that looked to offer a relative degree of security. The big cat settled down to view the proceedings: proceedings which, as time was to reveal, were to prove a sound lesson on how close Brother death skips along behind Brother error, that sly desperado who dances about in the minds of all creatures, mighty and humble.

Not a good half dozen crocodile lengths away, on the immediate edge of the thicket, a nearly full-grown lion appeared to be having difficulty overcoming a sable cow that he had obviously confronted too hastily for his own good! With a calf at heel, the doughty antelope was having none of it. While never taking her eyes once from the lion as he jerkily darted in and around her looking for an opportune avenue of attack - on her or her calf - she was keeping him stoutly at bay with the deadly, bowed horns that are the sable's pride; relentlessly driving vicious, lateral sweeps between she and her assailant. Beneath the bristling mane, her sumptuous, burnished bronze coat, swathed in perspiration, glistened in the sun.

With her deep chest, tapering hindquarters, and chalk-white facial markings smeared bold as war-paint, she looked the very epitome of wild thoroughbred beauty spiked to the brim with raw courage. Sable are the warrior antelope of the bush; certainly Umbulala's mother had told him as much. The lion cocked its head, confused. Doubtless he had never met a sable antelope before, nor heard of its reputation as a fighter. He shifted suddenly to the left of her; this time the sable seemed to falter, stumbling a little the opposite way. Without another moment's hesitation the lion moved in for the kill - not seeing it was a mock fall! Flashing a riposte as quick as lightning bolts across the night sky, the pointed head of the sable

cow swung round, brandishing horns like sabres - and lunged, finding her mark in one clean thrust of horn!

An agonized roar wrenched the bush through. Even from where Umbulala watched enthralled, the sound of escaping air at the impact of the sable's horns slamming through heart and lung was unequivocal. With the lion now neatly skewered, the sable lifted him up into the air. Then, with one mighty heave and flick of her elegant head, she tossed the body clean across the clearing - right into a thorn bush! Quickly trotting over to it, she proceeded with great flourish to run it through again and again with scythe-like sweeps of those deadly horns. Meantime all her calf appeared bent on doing was to dive under her belly to suckle, oblivious to the sweeping horns and the whole drama being played out around it!

Stamping the ground and jigging angrily about the carcass, her eyes bloodshot and bleary with battle, the sable was panting heavily. Only when sure of the lion's permanent state of repose did the antelope calm down, give a sharp snort of satisfaction, and then, with offspring in tow still complaining bitterly of its need to suckle, canter away.

Umbulala watched them go. A sable cow bringing a lion to bay, then killing it without the cat laying so much as a lascivious paw on her, wasn't one of your everyday things, and he was suitably impressed. But such an incident is not rare. Sable have often been known to come off victorious when set upon by lion; even two lions in the case of a big lone sable bull, when it has been known for both cats to get killed. And with nary a mark left on the sable - only a bent of sheer murderous intent.

It's the striking combination of horns - scintillating weapons in themselves - a fearless, fighting determination, and enough heart to keep an elephant going, that makes the sable antelope so indomitable. Warrior antelope indeed! To Umbulala's way of thinking they were, to be sure, the bravest and most wonderful looking antelope to ever grace the wilds!

When at last the enraptured cat
managed to shake off the spell
of admiration which had fallen
over him, he climbed down the
outcrop, crossed into the
thicket.........and ambled slowly
over to the limp body of the
dead lion. Now, leopards are
very adaptable creatures;
thereby lies their wit. Proud
predators though they yet be,
they also understand how, if

they are to survive long in the jungle, a little pragmatism goes a long way
towards serving that end.

Hence no wise leopard is so proud not to scavenge a free meal when the
opportunity presents itself; and when the pickings, as in this instance, are
unquestionably fresh. For Umbulala, here was one such opportunity.
Tearing at the carcass, he split it open along the breast, and immediately
started in eating the heart and liver. The sharp edge of his appetite satisfied,
he buried the lion's unsavoury entrails, its intestines, in a soft, loamy patch
of ground a little distance off and neatly covered it over. Returning to the
carcass he settled back to eat his fill.

No sooner had he done so when sounds of approaching hyaena scored the
air. It uneased him. It was more than just the memory of his fearful
experience in the den, when he was but a few full moons old. If leopards are
to count any in the jungle their enemy then indisputably, more than the
baboon pack - even the wild dog - hyaena qualify for that distinction. It's
an ancient animosity, its roots lost in the mists of time.

One appeared; she was alone. She stopped a little distance off, ignoring
the buried guts which hyaena will invariably nose out, dig up and eat. No.

This hyaena was concentrating all her attention on what was obviously the prize - the carcass Umbulala was feeding on. So agitated with ravenous impatience was the creature, she started jigging up and down and frothing at the mouth. Giggling in that hideous way of hyaena when food looms, she whined greedily:

"We have pups to feed, we have pups to feed. Leave some for us you cat of the shadows! *You who eats the heart of lion!*"

Umbulala spat back at her contemptuously, crouching closer to the carcass:

"Bah! He is the curse of a mother who didn't teach him of the courage of the sable!! Besides. What care I for the well-being of your squirming whelps. The stench of you and your kind makes me want to retch......!"

Umbulala got up from the kill and began to move away, mindful that more hyaena might yet arrive on the scene.

"Have the dregs if you so wish!"

he called back over his shoulder,

"One who, so conceited, could flaunt the honour of lion in the face of the likes of sable, deserves no more than to be left as scrap for the likes of you!"

The panther had only gone but a few paces, and already the hyaena was slavering over the carcass. Wrenching off great hunks of flesh with her powerful jaws, she bolted them down in a twinkling; going on to gorge herself until bloated in almost the same time. In between the scrunching and gulping and spluttering that accompanied her eating, she threw a heckling jibe after the retreating panther:

"Those pups you scorn - they might well consume you one day!!"

Umbulala's hackles rose. He spun round and made to mock charge the hyaena. She immediately fell back in the obsequious way of her kind; then turned tail and lolloped off, snivelling and gagging with fright as she went, much to Umbulala's delight. After all. Like any leopard worthy of the name, he didn't much care for hyaena.

Yet there was one thing he appreciated about the beasts. Nature provides the jungle with such animals for an important purpose: to keep it clean and free of carcasses which would otherwise fester and rot, pollute the jungle, and spread sickness. The hyaena provides an essential service to Mother earth, and thereby plays an indispensable part in nature's cycle of life. In the wilds, no creature, great or small, mighty or modest, takes precedence over another. Like the two sides of a leaf, each in its own way is special; an integral part of the whole. Without the one, there cannot be the other. While the sable is as much a warrior as the lion, the hyaena is as much a hunter as any cat.

The hyaena is a predator of startling efficiency, and not a mere "scavenger": a term used more to denigrate the beast for habits which appear unseemly, than as a description fairly reflecting its hunting prowess. While their social behaviour and method of killing is neither haphazard nor unsystematic, hyaenas have jaws and teeth of such power, they can crush to powder even the bones of elephant. It is thus in this way, with the aid, equally crucial, of vultures and jackals, ants and flies, that nothing is left to rot long in the jungle, to cloy and contaminate its chaste traces. And thus is nature rightly served.

THE BULLFROG's DILEMMA

There's wisdom in small things

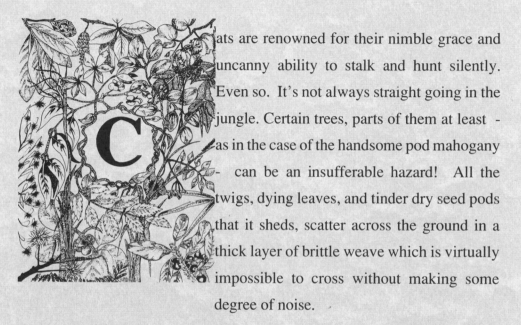

Cats are renowned for their nimble grace and uncanny ability to stalk and hunt silently. Even so. It's not always straight going in the jungle. Certain trees, parts of them at least - as in the case of the handsome pod mahogany - can be an insufferable hazard! All the twigs, dying leaves, and tinder dry seed pods that it sheds, scatter across the ground in a thick layer of brittle weave which is virtually impossible to cross without making some degree of noise.

The pods, of course, are a useful gift to the mahogany from Mother nature. They carry the tree's eye-catching seeds in hard, woody shells, or pods, which, as they grow, protect them from the ravaging attentions of birds and such like. Bi-coloured red and black, and unusually attractive, they are oft-called *lucky beans* by jungle folk. Once mature, the pod holding the seeds quickly begins to shrivel and die. Baked dry by the sun, it eventually splits completely open to scatter the seeds on the wind, thereby beginning the mahogany tree's life cycle all over again. Although many will be eaten, enough survive to take root where they fall. As for the broken pods left behind to hang dead and purposeless on barren stems, nature's ingenuity swiftly takes over.

The two halves of each empty pod quickly begin to twist and curl back on themselves until, dried brittle, they break from the stem and fall to the ground, forming what in time amounts to one of the simplest and most efficient alarm systems in the jungle. The slightest pressure brought to bear on any one part of this scrunchy network of scattered, tinder-dry pods immediately gives rise to a sharp report, guaranteed to alert any animal within earshot. Many's the fleet-footed prey that has taken flight in the nick of time from a frustrated predator as a result; foiled by nothing more than a dried-out mahogany pod! That jungle hunters should grumble is understandable. But what grounds they have for complaint is far outweighed by the gratitude of countless animals who owe their very lives to this neat warning system - delicately and cleverly wrought so that the odds aren't always stacked against the hunted.

It was just such a circumstance that one morning startled a herd of impalas into flight away from Umbulala. Honey-coated antelopes of smooth, athletic curve, they leapt away in smooth, black-heeled arabesques that arced with ease across a maze of vegetation, multifarious in form and fashion. Surprised by their sudden haste, Umbulala - not realising he'd been the cause of it - was as dazzled as ever by how high and how far they could leap in a single spring, clearing obstacles and distances that were the height and length of a full-grown elephant, and more! Indeed, at times it seemed as if impalas just jumped for the sheer joy of it, even when in danger; careering round and vying with each other

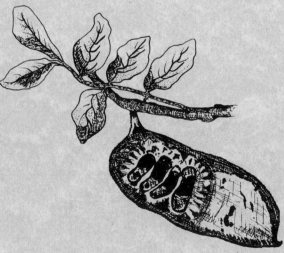

to see who could execute the highest or longest leap! Impalas have even been known to escape capture by turning about-face, in full stride, to leap right over their pursuer!

"Ah, the wonders of nature!",

Umbulala enthused, adding quietly to himself in more practical vein just what delicious eating they were. Sphinx-like felid.

Nearing the river, his gaze rifled through the vegetation on the bank, checking for anything out of place, or of interest. At the water's edge squatted a bulbous bullfrog. It appeared to be just gazing glinty-eyed into the murky traces, slime clinging like green baize to the rocks and logs that lay half-submerged in and around the river margin. Through the illusory, sun-effused mist of morning, the bullfrog had at first looked deceptively big, and Umbulala had initially taken it for a guinea-fowl.

But it was only a momentary sleight; the result of a fleeting aberration of light that's a common phenomenon in and around water on a hot, bright morning in sunny regions. Once the panther's eyes had adjusted to the play of light, memories of the happy times he had spent as a cub endeavouring to catch one or other of these slippery amphibians began to crowd his mind! He at once fell into a playful crouch; a sense of mischief had suddenly taken him over!

Creeping along by the shadow of a karee tree, the cat slipped down behind a stand of elephant grass toward the river. The thick sedge skirting its bank offered ideal cover for stalking the bullfrog! Very slowly, his strong, stout, paws sinking soundlessly in the mud, Umbulala edged up behind the unwitting bullfrog; still intently peering down into the water in search of food.......or some deeper philosophy. Little by little Umbulala eased himself closer in effortless silence, until finally - in reach of his quarry - he delivered one deft swing with an outstretched paw, and pinned the fat frog to the ground.

The panther's hold was firm, but gentle; and a warm chuckle of satisfaction rumbled up from within him:

"Ha....haaa!! At last I've caught you bullfrog! For a long time you and yours proved this cub an unworthy hunter, leading him a merry chase. Now, slippery one, 'tis Umbulala who laughs!"

The bullfrog shot frantic glances up at the big cat, no longer the cub of old, and desperately tried to squirm free. But its efforts were in vain - Umbulala had it pinned solid in the slime. The unfortunate frog just floundered and squelched about on its yellow belly, chubby legs flailing the air helplessly. Not one to give up easily when its life depended on it, the bullfrog had an idea.

"Oh, slay me not, great cat of the dark!!"
it cried out to its captor.

"You have indeed proved you are no longer a foolish cub, but a fine hunter; one that even the beasts of the water should rightly fear. But, like all jungle folk, I know of your fight against Kosi, and in that I can help you!"

Umbulala was intrigued. He knew the bullfrog to be a serious observer, and, moreover, an honest sort when its life hung in the balance.

"Tell me your story little one",
the big cat declared bemusedly,

"and indeed if there is anything in your tale I feel could benefit me in my quest, then I shall release you forthwith. If not, you shall remain where you lie, not squirming to be free as you are now - but split from end to end for the birds of the river, and the flies and ants to feed on!"
Umbulala stifled a mischievous chuckle.

"'Tis fair...'tis fair!...'tis fair!!"

repeated the bullfrog several times over like some phrenetic parrot, before launching into a burst of rhetoric calculated to save its life:

"Listen well mighty panther, if for no other reason than that this humble bullfrog should continue to breathe Mother nature's sweet air! Often I swim over there near that fallen tree at the edge of the river. *So* full of green weed and moss is it, that none but I can climb up onto it and not slip off. Now every time I'm there early of a morning, I always see Kosi coming down to drink. But unlike the other animals who also frequent the spot, he never uses the game path. Instead - doubtless to check out the surrounds first - he lies awhile on that rocky shelf beyond......"

The bullfrog rolled its eyes in the direction of a small outcrop a little way up the bank from the fallen tree.

"Once satisfied all's clear, he then steps down onto a stretch of sand below the shelf skirting the water's edge. Of course, from your height....."

it cheekily digressed,

"*you* should have little difficulty seeing it! At the moment I have to...craan.nn..nnne my neck.....!"

A firm squeeze of warning from Umbulala's paw brought the bullfrog up short. Any more sarcastic little departures like that, it said, and the next one would be permanent!!

"Uhmmm?? Oh!! Yy...yy-yesss!! As I was saying, *Brrrrother* panther" bullfrog swiftly continued........

"he steps down onto the sand and drinks his fill, all the while cursing Brother porcupine and his family for the pain in his mouth. Can't say I feel much sorry for him myself.....!"

Well, well! thought Umbulala as he pondered a moment on what he'd heard, gently rolling the bullfrog to and fro by way of a playful tease. The bullfrog's story excited him. Even the spot in question on the river he knew well. Releasing the bullfrog, he bade it go in peace, adding solemnly:

"May you witness the moment I set wrong to right."

Before plunging off into the water the bullfrog hesitated a moment to look up at Umbulala - its fat supercilious face puckered in respectful gaze. After all. It had this day communed eye-to-eye with death's messenger, and survived.

The black arc of night had long swept over the jungle when Kosi surprised and killed a dainty, blue duiker buck; one of the smallest breeds of antelope. The lion was on the verge of tucking into it when an eerie voice called quietly to him through the dark:

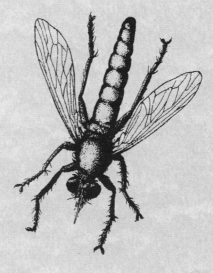

> "The time has come, Kosi, for my revenge......."

The lion spun round. There was nothing there. The bottomless well of night doesn't give up its secrets easily. A sudden rush behind him caught his attention; he swung back the other way. But the moon was blocked by the high ridge of a nearby kopje, making it impossible for him to catch even a glimpse of the wraith haunting him. Again a tormenting gibe floated across the gulf of night:

> "Here old one; up here in this tree.....enjoying your duiker!!"

It was the ultimate insult, and Kosi felt angered beyond belief. Right from under his very nose some dreaded interloper had stolen his kill, one he'd been starving for, and then bolted straight up the very tree he was standing under! Although tree climbing is a specialist skill of some lions, in general these big cats are far too heavy. Nor are they particularly agile enough. Such arboreal nymphs as do exist among lions are few, being exclusive to certain, small corners of Africa. And Kosi, his condition aside, was by no means one

of them. The tree in question was a veritable giant, with sheer branches reaching right on up and out of sight into the fathomless pitch of sky, and Kosi hadn't a hope in heaven of climbing it. All he could do was claw pathetically at its trunk; too straight and wrinkle-free for the lion to get even a foothold.

"Come now, cub killer!"

a cry wafted down from the depths of the tree's crown to taunt the lion again,

"did not the go-away bird that hops and clambers clumsily over the tops of thorn trees tell me that I'd supplied you with a bumper feast of baboon not so long ago? Well then! Just look upon it as repaying a favour."

Kosi's thoughts screamed,

"Sooo.....'tis that black fiend Umbulala who comes to torment me and make off with my kill!"

Kosi knew there was nothing to be gained wasting time trying to retrieve it. Instead, he must quickly set off again to hunt, before his hunger really got the better of him, and while he still had the advantage of the cover of night for stalking and ambushing prey.

In Kosi's ailing condition time and chance ran out far more quickly than is desirable for any cat. Not that Kosi wasn't fit. It was just that what goodness and strength his body drew from the small kills his crippled mouth forced him to subsist on, had to be fed and nourished all the more often. Besides. He frequently ended up covering a considerable distance before coming across game that was relatively easy pickings. When he did, he would plan his attack with all the skill of a master hunter; a knack that, despite his debility, he hadn't lost.

Presently he sighted a young bushpig. The way looked to be clear. Wasting no time, Kosi decided to take it out at once. But he hadn't reckoned on the stealthy panther, still secretly keeping pace with him. Slipping through the undergrowth, the lion had just got within pouncing distance when Umbulala let out an explosive, rasping yawl! It resounded like a clap of thunder through

the still of night, so sudden and so
bloodcurdling was it. Gripping the
atmosphere and every living thing
around with such a heart-thumping
sense of fright, not only did the pig
bolt for its life, but so did one old
buffalo, two sable antelope, and even
a full-grown elephant; the latter
trundling off trumpeting into the

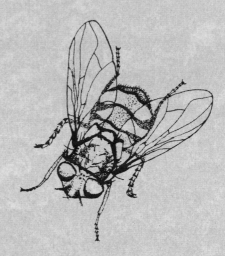

dark, with more than the odd note of discord embellishing its tone. Startled
fowls nesting in the overhanging trees took to flight; while from under scrub
and scattered patches of discarded bark and foliage, nightjars and numerous
small animals were flushed every which way.

When the ruckus finally died down, Kosi tried to draw the panther out; but
to no avail. Three more times that night the lion valiantly attempted to make
a kill, and at every attempt he was thwarted by Umbulala. Neither did dawn
bring respite. As the sun seeped slowly skywards, the lion felt on the verge
of despair. With fierce hunger pangs wracking his stomach, his morale was
at the lowest it had been; not helped by the knowledge that he'd now have
to hunt in daylight, under an increasingly hot sun.

"But at least......."

he sighed, bravely trying to buck himself up,

"it'll be easier to spot that infuriating panther, who's been doing his level

best to starve me to death! Ohhh!!! The curs of the jungle take him!"
Kosi checked himself. The one thing he mustn't do was give way to anger,
or unnerve himself, as otherwise he'd most surely end up fodder for maggots
before the day was out! To regain his equilibrium he tried to relax himself.
But after a brief spell he was up again - over-tiredness, what with his
nocturnal frustrations and everything else besides, had made him restless,
and he couldn't settle. To add to his miasma of misery a raging thirst had

taken hold.......and suddenly the lion was left with no alternative but to seek some relief from his ills. Giving himself a hearty shake by way of encouragement, he at once set off along a path that led down to the river.

By now the sun was well up and Kosi, having followed the game trail for some considerable distance, cut off through heavy bush offering a degree of shade, and on toward his favourite watering spot. He was a sorry figure. Bedraggled and weary-worn, with a walk more akin to a dull crawl than the proud gait of lion, Kosi's condition had taken a terrible toll; of his spirit, as much as his body.

For those who find acceptance of life's misfortunes impossible, constant pain can be such a soul-destroying affliction. Worse still, in Kosi's case, was how with time he had scratched his face raw in his frantic efforts to dislodge the quill embedded in his jaws; and this, coupled with a mouth and gums swollen and disfigured beyond belief, just aggravated his bitterness and anger more. In addition, festering sores inside his mouth refused to heal as the quill was continually piercing them, resulting in the suppuration reaching such a stage of infection, it was slowly seeping its poison into the lion's stomach.

Through the dappled cover of bush Umbulala observed his quarry. He felt a twinge of pity for the old brute. It was chastening to think that here before him was once one of the jungle's most magnificent and majestic of hunters. And the black cat sighed about the impermanence of life's fortunes, and how the mighty can be so easily brought low.

"But now old lion".........

he vowed resolutely under his breath,

"you won't have to wait long to see an end to your misery. No creature, even one whose own foolish conceit is the cause of an ill fate such as this, should suffer so and live. Shame on you Mother nature, and on you Mother earth - such misery is the curse of the world!"

Umbulala dashed on through the jungle, silent of tread and clear of purpose. On reaching the river well ahead of Kosi, he squatted low and carefully surveyed the scene up and down the bank nearest him. A little way downstream was the fallen tree lying prostrate, half-in, half-out the water. Set back a few paces up the bank from this, and angled down in a point toward the river's edge, was the granite shelf where Kosi had not as yet appeared.

With no time to lose, Umbulala slipped quietly into the river shallows so to deaden his scent; then, taking care not to make a sound, waded towards the spot where the shelf's stubby snout jutted tentatively out above the riverbank. Just at the point where a dry, narrow strip of beach came up along one side to meld with the river margin, the tip of the rock almost reached the ground. It was under here the cunning panther eased himself, his belly dragging in the soft slushy sand as he slithered out of the river shallows, right in beneath the granite overhang, his paws never once touching dry sand to leave any tell-tale tracks.

Slowly edging himself into the best position from which to strike, his firm, strong back scrapped a little against the rock above. Once settled, completely hidden in the overhang's cavernous shade, Umbulala's eyes fell on a set of lion spoor on the sandy strip of beach directly in front of him - but a butterfly's wingspan from his nose. Kosi's! What was striking about them was their sheer enormity. They were as big as lily pads and Umbulala, himself a mighty cat at half the size again of the average leopard, was singularly impressed.

One would never have guessed from the look of them that the owner was ailing. The pug-marks lay firm and steady on the dampish sand, well shaped and cleanly incised all around the edges; indicating an evenness of pressure that betrayed not a hint of injury or poor health. A lion will land on its victim all four, huge paws at a time. On scraping downwards in one simultaneous action, its claws working away like sickles, it will then inflict the most devastating wounds that in themselves can constitute the coup de grâce before the lion has even moved in to deliver the first bone crunching bite. This is something the wise hunter never forgets. Umbulala hadn't.

Taking a deep breath, he relaxed his muscles and listened to the silence. Only the soft, grey call of a dove mingling with the gentle lapping of the water a little way beyond him, dared to intrude. The hush of the surrounding quiet - verily crypt-like in character, so charged was it with a sense of foreboding - began to creep in on Umbulala, and he couldn't help concluding how infinitely awesome moments of truth are. He recalled the warning his mother had given him that morning, moons previous, when he left the family den for the last time; how sick as Kosi was, he was still a deadly adversary. Jungle lore is full of tales about the unbridled ferocity and courage of the leopard. Yet the lion, by comparison, with its sheer strength, size and unabashed confidence in its own brand of rule, can at times make the leopard - the jungle's ultimate carnivore - look like a cub. This is no less true of a lion that is old or injured. Any lion is deadly.

A shadow oozed across the sand. Kosi had arrived - and the unmistakeable odour of lion drifted down to the panther on a wisp of wind that presently died. In the same moment Kosi caught sight of the bullfrog, and let out a dismissive grunt.

"He would do well to be pleasant",
thought Umbulala,

"considering what secret the frog holds!"

While the panther watched, the shadow on the sand grew fatter as Kosi strolled down the rock towards its front edge, seemingly foregoing his customary habit of resting at the top. Umbulala braced himself. His heart pounded in his ears with apprehension - yet all his senses were as alert as antennae.

Kosi paused immediately above him on the overhang of the rock so to check the surrounding bush, before turning his attention to the river. There the most that moved were the familiar pastel traces of water lilies bobbing peaceably with the lazy mood of the water. Impatient as he was to ease the burning thirst in his throat, the lion took care not to hurry. Hard, tawny eyes scanned the river for the tell-tale lumps that spoke of crocodile, then flickered back in turn to the shore where they scoured the narrow ribbon of sand below for fresh spoor. The scene appeared to hold nothing untoward, and satisfied as such, Kosi crouched.

Stretching out a forepaw, he gingerly placed it down on the soft strip of beach to the left of Umbulala, still lying hidden directly beneath the rock. The sand squelched as the enormous paw found its purchase, tiny streams of alluvial flows oozing from between the claws with the bite of pressure on the sandy ground. Almost in the time it takes a dragonfly to flit from sight, Kosi moved to straddle the rock so to bend forward and drink - and at once the whole leg tightened. Balanced at an angle nose downward to the water, his two hind paws were poised nearly flat on the rock to the back of him. The lion had swung all his weight onto the one foreleg, and was in the process of bringing the other down to join it - this time to the right of the nose of the rock - when the panther struck!

In those fleeting moments between movements which, beginning with one, startlingly sharp burst of pain that as quickly again slurred into slow- motion, the lion was barely aware what had happened. With his head held up checking the surroundings, all that would have registered was a searing surge of agony that started in his neck, thence scudded burning through his body...........until every sinew of him smarted and roared rebellion at the horror of it! Yet those there that day recall hearing only the gurgled, strangled cry of an animal dying.

Like a buffeting force lightning propelled, Umbulala had struck from beneath, cleaving the lion's neck below the jaw from edge to edge, so to rip out the windpipe in one ferocious, thrusting wrench. Kosi didn't stand a chance. Stumbling almost the moment the panther hit him, his body arched. Suddenly whipping upwards, he hurtled forward through the air in a last convulsion of energy, as though sprung from a catapult; tumbling over himself in mid-flight, before plummeting down headlong into the river where he came up face to shore, his eyes bleary with the rapid onslaught of death that now gripped his body in terrible contortions.

Many things about life in the jungle at first seem inexplicable; not least the actions and activities of the creatures that inhabit it. And so it was now with Kosi, as he lay dying. Who knows, maybe it was that serene sense of resignation death brings; or perhaps just simple relief that his trial of a life should at last be ending. Whatever. The dying lion appeared to gain some strange, inscrutable satisfaction from the fact that the one responsible, now standing before him in the bloody shallows..........was Umbulala.

"The jungle need fear you, *cat of the shadows!*"

Kosi was heard to gasp, his body twitching in death's grip, his throat a gagging hole frothing blood.

"My pain is ending; yours is to live on.....to inspire envy and fear in those whose only desire will be to see you *die!*"

A last violent tremor wracked his body. The old lion crumpled - and died, only the watery traces to captain his spirit now.

For some moments Umbulala remained where he stood, staring across at the lifeless lion. By nature leopards are quiet creatures, not overly bellicose nor given to needless clamour; preferring instead the few yawls or grunts that are at times necessary to frighten game toward them, or away from them, whatever the situation demands. Certainly seldom growling to excess. But this day was different.

Umbulala glanced away into the distance towards his cubhood haunts. With the profoundest sense of an ambition achieved that he wished his nearest and dearest to share, the panther called across the stretch of time and billowing green between in rough, sawing coughs that spoke again and again:

"Kosi sleeps in the heart of Mother earth!"

The proclamation rang into every corner. The onerous deed was done, and Umbulala, his task now to forge out a territory of his own and win himself a mate, slipped away into the embracing mask of jungle.

Watching Umbulala depart, the bullfrog grinned - of the doings of this day it would expound much. As it turned out there was much to tell. The jungle learned how in time .....*'twas the slimy crocodile* that put the final touches to Kosi, ensconcing the dead lion deep underwater in a hollow in the side of the riverbank, until bloated and decayed to such a degree, the scaly saurian felt inclined to devour it in its entirety. As bullfrog would have it:

"And so it was, in the way peculiar to their kind since time immemorial, that spinning and twisting off chunks of flesh till none remained, the foulest of all did indeed feed well from that pitiful carcass."

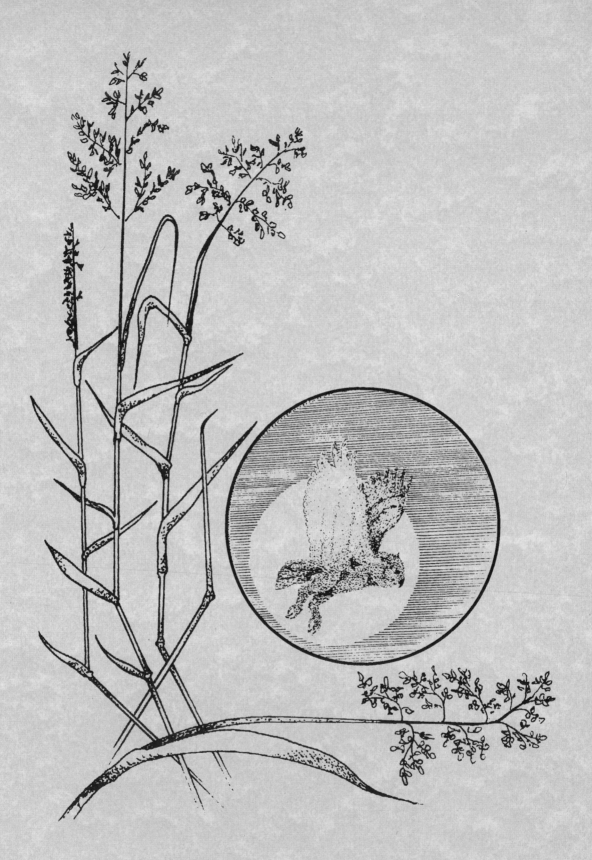

WHY

*Hope hangs like dewdrops
on the flower of life....*

bove the shadowy fringes of the jungle crown the merest shard of moon had begun to edge as Umbulala stepped out. Off amid the wilderness of undergrowth, a nightjar trilled its song. Skimming down to land on an elephant path winding along the ground like a shallow engraving, innumerable slots and divots plotted on it by huge feet offered fine fare in a surfeit of insect life. The night itself hung cool and cloudless beneath a sky buoyant with stars.

Everywhere the air seemed pinched with sounds in concert: birds of varying persuasion hooting to mates; jackals howling silvery arcs across the darkness; frog-song floating up from forest and pool - some of it hoarse and billowing, the best of it far off and delicate as wind-chimes tinkling. A distant hyaena giggled irreverently, sending zebras belling in alarm, brass gongs ringing in their throats; closer still a buffalo *whuffed* from a thicket, as down the spine of night blared a trumpet of elephant. Even shrill, chirruping cicadas added their characteristic timbre to the chorus, until it seemed as if only Umbulala moved through the jungle without making a sound, dense congestions of foliage, heavy with the damp of late evening, parting in a whisper before him.

With taut muscles rippling neath a coat of jet, his body lithe and powerful, the big cat stealed on through the undergrowth. Despite their size, the cat's broad, stout paws carried him over even the driest traces of leaves and twigs with such silent and graceful ease, the cat might have been woven from thistledown. Umbulala walked on his toes, as all cats do. Agility so refined, combining intelligence with eyesight and hearing honed to hair-trigger precision, and here indeed was a masterpiece moulded by nature.

The panther was not about hunting this night. He'd brought down a fine impala ram earlier in the day. Consuming a large portion of it, he'd secured the remains in a safe larder, high up in a mahogany tree, for later eating. Hence this night - this starry night that promised a hunter's moon round and ripe - Umbulala was about other things. There was the need to work off what had been a hearty meal, for one; the indolent feeling, too, that follows after one has imbibed well. Umbulala, with nothing in particular to do, wandered on, making the most of the opportunity to relax and ramble. Presently, he came on an area he immediately recognised as bordering his mother's and sister's territories. The big cat stopped; and thoughts suffused with the pull of pleasant memories past at once began to wash over him, questing his spirit on to some long-gone, yet familiar dimension. This meditative frame of mind stayed with him; for how long it's difficult to say because it was at that moment, without warning, it happened.

A shriek of unmitigated terror cleaved the night, wrenching its sanctity like a dust-devil driving across the land. It was a cry strange and new; a cry invested with a quality that sounded a prescience innocence doesn't cater for. Not the roar of attack. Nor the crash of a tree pushed to ground by elephant. Not even the thundering hooves of a herd of buffalo kicking up a storm. This sound was different. It was like nothing Umbulala ever

recalled hearing, nor wished to again, for it rung the heart through with a sense of unspeakable outrage. Yet, somehow, somewhere, mid the despair of that cry, there hung a fleeting note of oneness with every beast of the jungle.

An animal was dying; dying in some unbridled agony; dying, not in the selective way of the wild, but in terms profoundly unnatural. Just at what stage Umbulala realised it was leopard doesn't much matter; neither does the moment something in the tone of the cry lead him to swear it was his sister, Sibindi. Left with no time to wonder, Umbulala let fly through the jungle, forgetting nothing of his training in his haste - the lissom body manipulating with the lightning skill of a conjuror under and around leafy overhang and pockets of green.

Almost in conjunction with each other, the cat's senses raced quicker than thought. Unrelenting eyes gazed hard ahead, rifling through the foliage, their pupils dilated moons of jet. With hearing equally acute, Umbulala absorbed the sounds of the night, carefully sifting every nuance. Even the fine, sensory hairs sprouting like down inside his ears alerted him to any sudden change in wind direction, however slight. This meant that he could always move at an angle where it favoured him best. Long vibrissae on the panther's muzzle worked as feelers, gauging the width of openings before him, and warning of obstacles in the way.

He worked his path deliberately into the night breeze, not with it - catching, as he did so, every scent as Brother wind whistled back over ears pasted flat against his head:

"With caution, hunter of the night......with caution......"

It was a warning not without significance. Umbulala had scented the merest trace of a presence on the back of Brother wind so instinctively unnerving, he needed no superior powers of deduction to connect it with the unearthly, bloodcurdling scream still ringing cold in his ears. Hairless ape were in the area; his very instinct screamed it. Memories of the great Bulala, and of the

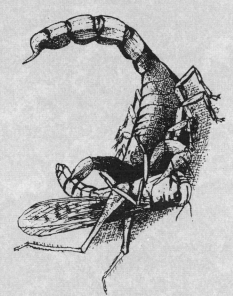

unjust ways of the hairless ones flooded his mind - and a bitter anger surged within him. But Umbulala was a hunter for which such emotion is never a boon. And with that innate talent for self-command that is the guiding star of the hunter and seeker, he quickly checked himself. Mother nature had missed nothing in her design.

Boasting the leopard's uncanny knack of being able to trace the precise origin of a sound, Umbulala made straight for the place from where he was certain the cry had come. En route he caught sight of, out the corner of his eye, something sitting upright on the branch of a dead tree. He had at first taken it to be a cat of sorts, a caracal: thick body, large head and protruding ears silhouetted against a starlit sky. Only when it shook itself did Umbulala recognise the eagle owl. A wary bird with a sharp, inquisitive mind, it is an an expert observer with exceptional binocular vision, especially at night. The eagle owl comes of a specialised family of avifauna famed for mastering the art of silent flight; cleaving evening's shadow like ghostly apparitions of themselves. Umbulala slowed his pace and called out to the masterful bird:

"Whoa......Sister owl - help a fellow hunter with wise counsel!"

The plea was barely out before the owl was swivelling its large head around to look directly over its back, all the while searching the darkened ground below for the enquiring hunter. Such unique mobility compensates for the owl's inability to rotate its eyes - haunting, cat-like things like fiery orbs eclipsed by ebony moons. As the panther's senses raced with the urgency to be on the way again, time dragged snail-like as the eagle owl blinked its huge eyes over and over, adjusting and re-adjusting focus to pin-point the caller. At last spotting the crouching cat it hooted:

"Twoo-hoo!! Umbulala?!"

a touch amused by its own laxness,

"you...whoo...whooo are hard to see at night! What can I do for you, hunter of the shadows?"

Umbulala explained. When he'd finished, eagle owl bided a moment before replying, as though seeking to give shape to thoughts that would run a shiver through the jungle heart.

"There were two hairless apes in the gully beyond"

went the owl's account,

"and early in the day, one of their traps caught an animal - a leopard heavy with cub......."

Umbulala's eyes shone through the dark. They spoke volumes.

"Yes....your sister Sibindi, I now realise. Time passed. Then, not long after evening had fallen, they found her. Immediately they began to prepare a small fire not far from the snare in which she was trapped; a strange, square shape of air boxed in by many sticks crossed this way and that."

Umbulala learned that the sickened scream he'd heard was a panic-stricken cry of fear and pain as the hairless apes suddenly caught hold of Sibindi by the tail. Wriggling and scratching in mortal terror, they wrenched her backwards against the side of the trap that held her, took a burning poker from the fire - and thrust it into her, ramming it in under the tail and right up inside her to kill the big cat and her unborn in the most despicable and heinous way known to the jungle.

Bile flooded Umbulala's stomach, rushing to his throat. He enquired hoarsely of the owl:

"Ttt..t..tell me, wise one. You know much about many things.......why, *why* did they do this??"

Eagle owl sighed heavily.

"Oh Umbulala! From what I could tell, all they wanted of Sibindi was her hide. In this unnatural way they don't damage the fur. It's called a perfect skin, I've heard say. What is stranger, they haven't even eaten her?! Instead, her carcass lies naked by the ant-heap; left for the scavengers to slavishly consume. I'm sorry Umbulala. The ways of the hairless ones are not for us to understand."

Umbulala remained where he was, very still, as if frozen into stone. After awhile he implored the owl:

"Oh, bird of the great shadow - aid me in ridding the jungle of these wanton curs!!"

Peering down at the cat through shining sovereign eyes that perceived the other's distress, eagle owl responded without hesitation:

"That I do pledge brother panther - from my heart."

When Umbulala found Sibindi's body, he stood for a moment transfixed, his senses awash with shock and outrage. For one who was no mawkish sentimentalist, such feelings ran deep and true; like the chill in his heart. Of more far-reaching significance was the anger waking within him - anger, cold and incredulous that animal could so treat animal with such ignominious indifference. Before him was a crude, skinless carcass that lay like a boil on the jungle face. No longer the sleek Sibindi - but a mute, gelatinous lump, its tight, pink flesh suffusing blue like a suppurating bruise, the white tissue striated with driblets of blood that flecked it like wisps of red dust. Eyes once full of spirit, now deadpan and lifeless, protruded with gruesome melancholy from the skeletal head

to which flesh still clung, pinched and exposed - wincing at being sullied so. From a jaw little more than skin-bedraggled bone, bared teeth stared frozen in a grimace that spoke emptiness.

"Ah, those teeth......",
reflected Umbulala,

"that wrecked havoc among the baboon troop in the great fight......"
He stopped short - he must think only of what was to be done, not what had been done.

He shook himself vigorously, as if shaking off the dread of it all. Gripping hold of the carcass at the back of the neck, he began to drag it away in the direction of a baobab he'd noticed some distance back from the ant-heap; eldrich tree that often under the most needful circumstances had proved a friend to many a jungle creature. On reaching it, he rested an instant to catch his breath. He then climbed, carcass in tow, and left it to rest - enfolded in the bosom of the great tree's branches, and shielded from the jungle's plundering packs. Leaping down, he hurried back to where he'd left eagle owl - but one burning question filling his mind:

"Noble owl - where might a cat find these hairless ones who so desecrate the sanctity of our domain?"

The owl had not been idle in Umbulala's absence. It had, in fact, undertaken a reconnaissance flight to provide the panther with up-to-date information on the movements of the hairless ones.

"They still bide at the same place, not more than ten elephant paces from fool's land where the surface is false, and where too, those without a mind to take care are swallowed whole into the bowels of Mother earth. Just now, in the strip of clearing flanking it, they were crouched by a fire, sprouting smoke and laughing together of their great hunts. Bah! They are not hunters who kill only to defile and scrounge....!"

Umbulala licked his paws in solemn succession, pondering the possibilities of fool's land. Eagle owl watched the pensive cat embroiled in his

thoughts.....and it didn't take much
for the wily raptor to guess along
what lines they might be working.
Thus, shortly before Umbulala
slipped away to seek the strangers
out, the owl proffered an observation
it felt the panther might do well to
remember:

"I landed on a tree above
them........."

it began tantalisingly,

"and on noticing me, one immediately began to throw stones at me,
exclaiming that an owl is a bad omen! Bah! Bad omen indeed! The
other ape just laughed, claiming to believe quite the opposite; that an owl
meant good fortune!"

It was the flickering reflections of the fire Umbulala caught sight of first.
He had streaked through the bush with all the resolve of one sworn to confront
the challenge of a lifetime head on. Only on glimpsing the fire's glow
through the trees did the absoluteness of events about to unfold come home
to him. He stopped just short of the clearing where the jungle also halted; as
though itself shrinking from the dangers of the land beyond the grassy verge.

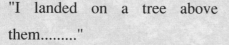

The hairless ones were hunched over the fire exactly as the eagle owl had
told him, silhouetted in its incandescence. The pair, as best the panther could
judge, seemed oblivious of any presence. For all that, they were exchanging
noises one-to-one like the monkeys do; and so loud and so disproportionate
to their size, Umbulala wondered if it might be some ploy to frighten off any
unwelcome visitors. Brother wind ceased blowing altogether, and from out
of the fire a trunk of grey smoke began to eerily rise and waft heavenward.

In the distance a jackal bayed - and an ominous chill began to take hold of the night.

The hairless ones stood up. Being the first he'd ever seen, Umbulala was shocked! These most feared of animals looked to him but frail creatures, with no canines or claws to speak of, and who walked upright on two skinny legs - just like the herons!

"Are these the creatures that strike down the mighty elephant and other giants of the jungle with but a blow??!"

Umbulala asked incredulously of the eagle owl, who'd just that moment alighted on a nearby stump.

"Beware Umbulala......"

the bird hastened to warn him,

"they are without doubt the most ruthless of all Mother nature's animals. Even the great forests and the powerful rivers are prey to their might; while the mountains, too, are made to tremble and quake as they rip out her internals."

Umbulala shuddered.

"I doubt not what you say, wise one, for the great Bulala warned me long ago to leave the hairless ones well alone. But tell me bird of the night....?"

a thoughtful Umbulala wondered aloud,

"do they know of the earth beyond them that eats animals?"

Eagle owl blinked for a time, then replied:

"I think not. I overheard one mention the area to the other, who indicated it was buffalo country from the look of some spoor that had been found nearby. And if such was the case, the ape claimed to have no wish to be caught out on open ground by those monstrous oafs!"

Umbulala caught the gleam in the owl's eye, and like one secretly enjoying with a cohort the clue to the charade, chuckled delightedly to himself.

By now the apes had turned their backs, and were gazing across at the forest on the other side where, if the degree of noise rising from that segment of the night was anything to go by, an elephant had just rammed a tree down with a resounding crash. All else was silent; even frog-song ceased dashing silvery apostrophes across the night.

So engrossed were the apes, they continued to stare blindly into the void of night before them; as if waiting for it to suddenly burst into light and give of its secrets. With their backs turned and their minds thus occupied, the panther recognised his chance. Giving vent to a wrath that until this moment had lain dormant within him, he unleashed an almighty roar, the fire of which set the atmosphere to tremble like air in a heat haze. With eyes and sickle-spiked claws and fangs flashing sinisterly in the moonlight, the big black leopard oozed forward.

The apes reeled round. There, like a shadowy, mystery wraith, the cat hung before their unwitting eyes. Neither had ever been confronted by such an unnerving sight; neither had ever heard of a black leopard nearly the size of a lioness, let alone ever seen one! Thus for two who could wonder at the ominous intent of a harmless owl, the choking fear of the netherworld engulfed them. As far as they were concerned the forces of ju-ju, of the supernatural, were upon them; and in the jungle such forces have potency. Had they not just trapped and violently killed a leopard? And now, like some vengeful, black spirit-cat of the night, one materialises out of the numinous abyss of jungle - and attacks them!

Without heart or will to arm themselves, deadly superstition having taken hold, they turned and ran like creatures demented.

Although Umbulala might well have concurred with the notion that nature has provided the hairless ones with efficient legs - for all their odd shape - he could have outpaced them in but a few strides. Instead he chose not to. Carrying his charge right up to the swamp's edge, there he halted; not the slightest intention of laying a claw on the apes. Why sully his humour further. Let nature deal with them as nature saw fit. In grim silence the panther bided on the brink of fool's land, an orange glow investing the sleek, spectral form as it sat-stood, silhouetted in the firelight.

The apes had not gone fifteen paces into the swamp when a new fear gripped them. In their frenzied terror they'd been barely conscious of the damp sand sucking and dragging inauspiciously under their feet. Suddenly aware of what horror fate had in store for them, they tried to turn back the way they'd come, in a frantic bid to reach dry land. With arms flailing wildly above their heads, each desperately fought to find a foothold. But in their rabid panic, screams and struggles only served to sink them deeper into the uncompromising sand. Truth makes losers out of fools. Mother earth was not giving up her catch; she too had heard Sibindi's bewildered and pitiful cries.

All the while Umbulala sat quietly watching, waiting.....a solemn, umbral figure hovering before the flames. Silence soon fell over the swamp - only a solitary, sinewy hand, grasping the air, disturbing its mood. It stopped momentarily above the sullen rim of sand, as if breathless in anticipation, before sinking deftly from view into the bowels of the swamp, where only the choking sand sings a requiem for those it buries.

Umbulala turned away toward the jungle. In the light of the dying fire he caught sight of Sibindi's skin stretched pegged out on the ground. Angrily ripping it free, he cried across the stretch of night to the eagle owl, still perched on the tree stump:

"Of what use is her hide to hairless apes? And why....like this.....??!"

Eagle owl remained silent a moment - then called back to the bewildered cat in a chill tone:

"In your question lies your answer, Umbulala. You have seen how these creatures boast no coat of fur or feathers like us. Like symbols, or proofs of power which drives them to steal into the very skins of others - they wear it!!"

Nothing, it seemed to Umbulala - *nothing* was sacred to the hairless ones. They will take the very coats from the backs of other animals! And at the realisation, time all but stood still. Only Brother wind spoke a votive chorus across the jungle tops. Umbulala's thoughts flew to his mother. What would she make of it all, he wondered?

He thanked the eagle owl for its wise counsel and help. Gently picking the skin up between his teeth, the bitter tang from its coating of salt rudely stung his tongue and mouth. He returned it to its rightful place across Sibindi's body, still cradled in the bountiful heart of the baobab - an undisturbed repose its charge - thence left that part of the jungle swiftly as he'd come, never to return to it again.

THE WINDING WAYS

Despair wanes when courage wakes!

In the small hours Umbulala killed an adolescent kudu, having ventured down from the high, hill country he favoured, to the more open woodland of the lower reaches. By the time dawn had crept out from under the coverlet of night to awaken the jungle, he'd already consumed a goodly portion of the carcass, the exertion of the hunt having left him feeling more than just a little hungry! Despite his fill, he was determined not to leave any of it for the scavengers, and so he set about, before the day got too light, dragging the remains off to a safe depository in some generous tree.

Nothing deterred him in his efforts - neither thorn bush or scrub; nor the crossing of a dried-up creek, the steep banks of which proved particularly difficult to negotiate while endeavouring to manipulate a fair-sized carcass. Umbulala found the best method to adopt was to grasp the dead animal by the throat and walk astride it, leaving the cumbersome trunk of the body to trail behind between his forelegs. From time to time, when this proved too taxing, the big cat would about-face, doubtless prescribing to the notion that a change is as good as a break, and proceed backwards dragging the carcass after him. Unfortunately this way was almost as laborious as the other!

Stumbling into a fine stand of mopane woodland, the cat rested at the base of one strapping specimen, the height of which one was given some measure

of by the fact that the tree's bottommost branches looked to be well out of reach of most elephant; although that's not to say one such giant couldn't mow the tree down with ease to get at them! After all, among jungle creatures it is the elephants that are primarily responsible for the extensive reduction of woodland to scruffy, gnarled scrub.

Umbulala stifled a chuckle. Sharing his path was a very determined dung beetle - trundling backwards. With its hind legs it busily rolled ahead of it toward some burial place an ever-increasing ball of animal droppings. Inside the tightly packed dung walls, if not destined for the beetles own consumption, females of certain species lay their eggs during the mating season. In this way the larvae are assured of a plentiful food supply. On hatching, the young beetles simply eat their way through the walls of the dung ball. *Phew,* thought Umbulala, engrossed as he was in the activities of the small scarab, and not a little relieved that such industriousness and tenacity wasn't matched by a size comparable to elephant - also with a penchant for rolling all before them.

Turning his attention back to the tree, the cat eyed it for stowage possibilities. He couldn't help marvelling how like butterflies the mopane leaves were, with their alternate twin-winged shape. They were rich fodder for large numbers of buck, too, and not just mopane worms. Unfortunately at this time of the season, despite the tree's size and maturity, its crown's normally dense cover of foliage was somewhat on the thin side. But Umbulala contented himself with the generous height of the mopane, and returned to thoughts of the kudu carcass and the arduous task of dragging its deadweight up the bole of the tree, so to lodge it safely in a high fork.

With the sun yet barely above the horizon, it was a matter best attended to before temperatures started soaring to the dizzy heights customary in the lower altitudes. Gripping the young buck by the throat, Umbulala twisted and turned until he eventually manipulated the partially eaten carcass across his back. Shaking it into a position that felt firm, yet comfortable, the cat

gathered all his strength and concentration, and sprang up the tree trunk. The leopard's tough, tensile claws showed their worth; striking deep into the bark as, neatly and methodically, he shinned up the tree. A couple of leopard lengths up, he stopped at what looked to be a good refuge for his catch, in amongst a wide conflux of branches. Wedging the carcass in, he settled back on an adjacent limb to catch his breath.

Presently, equilibrium regained, Umbulala began the elaborate ritual of licking himself all over in that self-conscious way of cats, large and small. He licked away the sweat from the spongy underparts of his paws to cool himself, relaxing in between with mock assaults on the kudu carcass. Cuffing its head from left to right with one or other of his broad forepaws, memories raced to mind of his carefree cubhood; of those moments spent dashing lightning assaults on whatever might be littering the den floor, be it leaf or bone.

Despite his trenchant mood of whimsy, Umbulala was acutely aware that time was not for the wasting. So, once refreshed, pleasant fantasies were discarded for the more sober regimen of everyday survival. Before taking his leave, he checked that the buck's body was held snugly in the fork, climbing over and around it a number of times like some fastidious mud hornet securing her nest. When, finally, he slipped down the bole of the tree, and away through the cover of mopane to sleep part of the day away elsewhere, the morning sky was already a scarlet sash encircling the jungle.

Tentatively he nudged the slime aside with a forepaw, and lapped thirstily at the water. Umbulala had stopped at a stagnant pool to drink. A huge baobab, glorying in a bountiful expanse of branch and bough, loomed up

behind it. As he drank, the panther quietly eyed the monstrous tree. He found nothing to concern him. Climbing it, the big cat chose a broad, stout limb in amongst the baobab's shadowy, hospitable crown to stretch out on. The cool, tight skin of the branch seemed to meld to his shape as he straddled it; and for once in his now solitary existence Umbulala gave himself over to that delicious, inexpressible sensation of feeling wholly the responsibility of another.

The panther gazed thoughtfully at the skyline. Dawn's florid flush was fast ebbing away as the sun worked its way up into the heavens, the moon looking to be nothing more than a timid, circlet of gauze on the run from the brilliant usurper of its celestial crown. Lulled by the mood, the panther closed his eyes and dozed.

When he awoke, afternoon was upon the jungle. Heat distorted the horizon, twisting trees and kopjes into shimmering images that trembled and danced in the hot, sticky air. From his vantage point high up in the baobab, Umbulala could track the route and distance he'd covered that morning. He had followed the river margin upstream, and the vegetation had gradually become thicker and more and more dotted with high rocky protrusions - some pitted and gorged, others with sheer perpendicular faces splashed with moss and lichens that rose on up out of the maze of bush like silent exclamations.

In amongst this weave of trees and scrub and imposing ridges quested the river, and Umbulala's well-developed sense of smell led him back towards it with little difficulty. Many was the sunrise of late that had dusted the dawn, and not brought with it the hope of rain, and as Umbulala wandered along, he noticed how the effects of the drought were beginning to show even in these lush parts. Even the river appeared to be suffering; looking but a stream in comparison to the robust waterway of several full moons back.

Peering down at it from atop a gnarled embankment he'd wandered onto, the panther concluded it was too steep a drop to the water. Still feeling a little sluggish from his long nap, he lingered awhile; taking in the view and

enjoying its peace - an almost subliminal requisite of a cat's life. A school of hippos frolicking in the shallow water a short distance upstream caught his attention. Unfortunately, the hulking water-pigs were hardly nymphing blissfully in the hyacinthine wallows! With the level of water as low as it was, they were really pushed to keep themselves wet all over, a chore 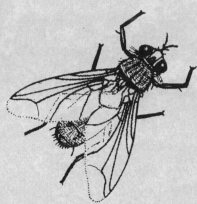 which hippopotamus must attend to daily if their tough, leathery hides are not to blister and split from unrelieved exposure to the sun.

The embankment rose sharply, and trying to locate an easy approach down to the river wasn't getting easier. Dreamily the panther slunk along, allowing Brother error to dance in his mind. He came up on a bluff. Directly below, a small herd of elephant was quenching its thirst and generally gadding about in the shallows. Their leader, the herd matriarch, was standing just out of the water sucking up trunkfuls of sand. In patent disregard of appearance, she was dusting herself all over to keep insects at bay, and relieve the irritant itching of old bites. Behind her in the river the rest of the herd was occupied in a friendly free-for-all in the water - in between drinking in deep draughts of it - with the young calves squealing delightedly.

"What a wonder that snout of theirs is!" enthused the panther, in obvious admiration of the elephant's trunk, and now dangerously distracted by the lazy mood of the day.

We feel our lives in waves, it's true to say, and Umbulala's at this moment was imbued with a sense of harmony dangerously free of worry. It is often such moments that often disguise the most deadly dangers; moments that would be barely perceptible if not for the rude interaction of calamity. When the fates juxtapose in malevolent guise, the animal off guard stands the most vulnerable.

From somewhere beyond his perception something forceful and heavy suddenly struck Umbulala full in the ribs; severely winding him and dealing the cat such a powerful clout, it knocked him completely off balance. Kuluma the python, resting anonymously nearby, had sensed the panther's distracted mood. Seizing its opportunity, it had launched an all-out attack on the panther.

Darting quickly forward, the snake had thrown its full weight at the cat's flank, seizing him with its long sharp teeth, not to inflict fatal wounds, but to get a firm hold. A python's strength is prodigious; the immensely long body - as long as a giraffe is tall - is one strip of muscle. Weighing as much as a small to medium-sized leopard, and more, a python coils round and round its captive, squeezing and constricting as it does so. The victim is either strangled, or killed due to its blood vessels bursting. Not an attractive proposition either way - and Kuluma the python was of such an inclination.

But, as skilful a hunter as the python was, it had made one sorry miscalculation. At the moment of attack, Umbulala had been standing on the very edge of the embankment, gazing down in rapt contemplation at the elephants several leopard lengths below. So close was the cat, that with the force of the thrust from behind, he lost his footing. Toppling sideways off the bluff, Kuluma, holding fast where it had viciously struck Umbulala in the flank, was now powerless to twine itself around the panther and squeeze the life out of him!

Thus locked together, cat and snake were plunging through the air toward the sandy riverbank before Kuluma fully realised it. Suddenly too late to avert the misadventure, the python knew it mustn't let go of the panther at any cost. Given the chance, and the mobility to do so, Umbulala was capable of parting the snake's head from its legless body with just one bite!

Umbulala's mind was turning somersaults. Precisely at what instant he'd learned the identity of his attacker, since a sharp thud to his ribs had brought his dreaming senses screaming back to reality, he couldn't say. All he knew

was that he was now in desperate peril of losing his life; a life first his mother, and latterly he had been doing their level best to keep functioning! Well.......maybe not exactly to date, he had to agree to himself in the light of *this* predicament.

But even the wisest make mistakes, or so it is said. And isn't that supposed to be the best way to learn",

"If one survives the mistake",
Umbulala's thoughts teased him. Pious prattle about a lesson well- learned being a lesson well-remembered is of little consolation when one is teetering on the brink of extinction, not knowing if one's going to survive to recall whatever lesson it is one's supposed to be learning!

"So that's life Brother panther!"
he thought he heard the wind whisper as it whisked past him.

"And one must have the grace to accept whatever life dishes out, smack on the snout - turning adversity to one's favour wherever one can!"
The cat couldn't believe his senses!

"Are you kidding!!"
he scoffed back, not entirely sure it was the wind he was addressing, or himself.

"Here I am, hurtling helplessly through space, with the added delight of having the jaws of some grasping python stuck in my side, and you have the temerity to sprout such sanctimonious nonsense about turning adversity to one's favour?!!"

As it was, all the bemused panther could see before him was thin air - and elephants. Elephants!!? The realisation all but screamed at him. And instantly he knew what to do. In the circumstances no risk could exist - even one involving elephants - that wasn't worth taking.

One of the more absorbing mysteries of life is its ability to stretch itself in moments of danger from what, in reality, is no more than heartbeats in time, to something seemingly like infinity. While still airborne, Umbulala let out a calculated, heart-thumping roar which reverberated along the hollow underside of the embankment to set in motion an immediate skirl of trumpeting from the elephants below.

Those elephants in the water launched into an abrupt stampede away from the bluff, just as Umbulala and Kuluma crash-landed in a heap at the matriarch's feet. The cow, whose innate reaction was to defend her herd come what may, straightway slewed round to face the anonymous aggressor, lifting great legs like ponderous, battering rams up and down on the sand. As her huge feet pounded and stomped away furiously, spurting grit and pebbles in every direction, the confused matriarch had no idea, in the commotion, the heat and the dust, what was actually happening; what had spirited an apparent attack on herself and the herd; nor who might be the cause of it! It had all come down on her like lightning out of the blue.

Being a relatively short drop, the fall from the bluff hadn't been a bad one; the soft sand cushioning the landing somewhat. At the first opportunity, Umbulala, dragging the python behind him with its jaws still savagely gripping his flank, darted under the nearest foot of the cow that wasn't on the ground - then straight out the other side just as it came down with a squelching "splod" right on top of the unfortunate snake trailing at the rear! The python gasped in agony, immediately releasing its grip on the panther. Slicker than thought, Umbulala bolted to safety; survival - not Kuluma's annihilation, nor concern for the searing sensation in his ribs - his only goal. Given the old matriarch's murderous mood, the longer he lingered, the greater the risk to his life. And he wasn't about to risk it yet again!

As for Kuluma, its huge attacker would have been virtually anonymous, registering at such close quarters as little more than a blurred mass of grey looming overhead. Only with its auditory senses - "hearing" curiously perceived via the tip of its tongue - and its much finer sense of smell through an organ in the roof of its mouth, would the python have some vague notion what was happening. And vague it certainly would have been, as pain would have dulled much of its comprehension of final events.

The more Kuluma writhed and curled its great long body in contortions - its coils so rigid with the flexion and contraction of nerve and muscle, and so bent double they reached on up in waves to pound under and at the elephant's chest - the more convinced did the old cow become of being attacked. She pummelled, and ground, and stomped at the desperately twitching snake with even greater urgency......until Kuluma lay like a gory mosaic, not very prettily painting the sand.

The python, like the leopard, is a formidable and powerful predator with as much degree of chance in its favour as any. When two such predators meet, they pool their chances. While the herbivore attacked by a predator has only one objective, to escape death; when predator meets predator in contest it is a fight to the death for both, and both know it! Fate is easier with the lamb.

The attack by the python had left Umbulala in severe pain. The ribs to the right of his chest were badly battered; while the skin and flesh around where the snake had grabbed and held him was punctured and swollen. Moreover, the awkward way he'd fallen had left him bruised and aching all over. On making good his escape from the python, and the seething maelstrom of elephant, the panther had staggered on through clumps of waxy combretum, bamboo thickets and bush. He soon found himself a secure lair tucked in an outcrop of rocks on the edge of the mopane woodland, and not far from the tree where he'd secreted the remains of the kudu.

Here he eased himself in; lying back into the cool privacy of his own solitude. The thought of his carelessness, and of how close Brother death had come, nagged at him until it came to feel like an old friend. He had learnt the lesson after all. Within a couple of days the pain had subsided sufficiently for Umbulala to feel a bit like his old self again; only now his stomach was complaining bitterly - and suddenly he had cause to be grateful for something else. Surely kudu would never taste so good!

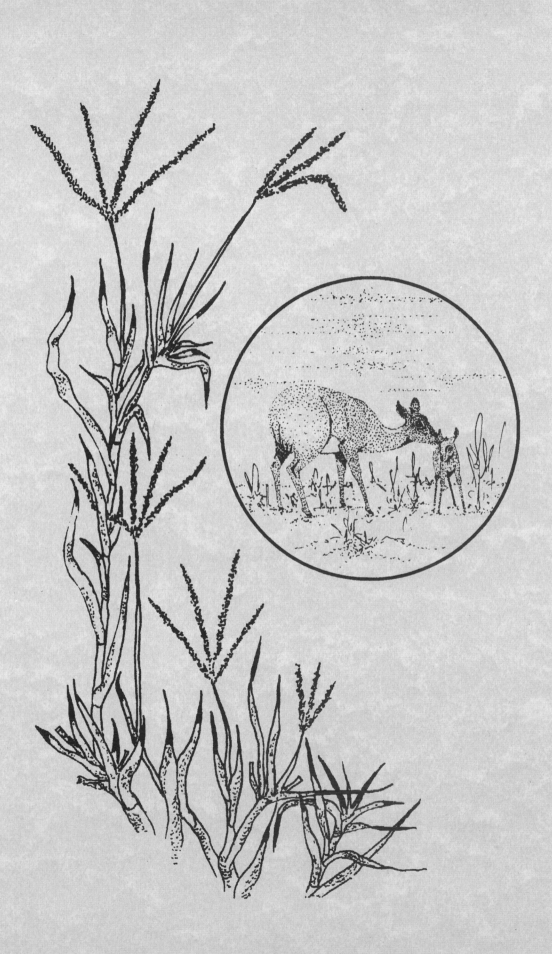

WHAT THE SWALLOW SAYS

Perfection.........
like the butterfly,
fleeting and whole

Umbulala's territory was extensive. Its range, working at a leisurely pace, could take anything up to one full moon to cover. Killing to eat once in every four to five days, he had no need for anything bigger. Moreover, it was rich terrain, boasting ample game, and Umbulala was coming to know its generous traces as intimately as any cat can; any cat unashamedly master of all it surveys. Regularly checking it out, and updating scent and scratch marks, he zealously guarded his territory against those of his ilk that might dare to harbour covetous designs upon it, and deport themselves accordingly.

Being a creature more of subtle whim, than one that could be labelled predictable, or fixed of habit, favourite look-outs and places to rest and sleep, stow a kill, or groom his claws emblazoned its extent. It was to one such hold-out that Umbulala hastened some days after his crushing encounter with the python. Cloistered high in a long bronzed kopje mantled end to end with sculptured crags, and flanking the brooding plateau country that hung blue and purple over the jungle, it offered the ideal refuge in which to sleep off the remains of the kudu, as well as effect a full and proper recovery in sure and safe seclusion. There is no more private creature than the leopard under par.

It was a cave not unlike the den in which he'd spent his cubhood. A sense of this pervaded the place, giving it an atmosphere of comfortable security which Umbulala found irresistible. Being snug and well hidden, in a veritable fretted fortress of rock, simply confirmed it as the perfect lair for a cat in want of re-charging his reserves away from the prying eyes of the wild!

At its innermost end the cave narrowed to a slender natural passage, presumably formed when Mother nature had tossed the great rocks up from under earth's crust to create the rugged terrain. Just ample enough to take Umbulala at a low crouch, it meandered deep into the bowels of the kopje, leading out the other side under a rocky overhang, or ledge, which formed part of an outcrop high up among a clutch of granite boulders worn smooth by the timeless caress of Brother wind. Here, succulent euphorbias, each like ritual candelabrum, lifted their branches in homage to the sun. They crowded almost to the top, scattering down again over the rocky humps and crevices of the slopes, their rugged traces licked aflame by brilliant bursts of wild aloes flowering vermilion. Further down on the lower slopes grey-green palms, spiky-crowned, fringed the kopje edges in stumpy ranks, before dank bush reached up to swallow the rest. Everywhere in between everlastings winked rosy-hued and yellow at the sun.

The cave was spacious enough. When the panther stood with his head held well up, his ears just brushed the roof. Secluded, yet at the same time not far down to the river, it had the advantage of not one, but two escape routes in both of the entrances, with the approaches to each too steep for scavengers to negotiate, and their opening spaces just that bit too small for lion to enter easily. Dominant predators in jungle hierarchy

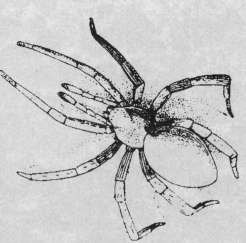

though they may be - owing more to size than greater cunning or hunting prowess - there were no lions to speak of in this verdant and fairly isolated neck of the woods. Although all cats will wander beyond familiar bounds, few lions bothered to stray so deep into the jungle - unless sick, like Kosi, they saw an obvious advantage in the area's seclusion and lack of competition from other lions.

Thus it was indisputably the panther's domain, and that's the way he hoped it would remain for a long time to come. "Yes, an ideal hideaway!" he cheerfully confirmed to himself as he'd made his way there through the more open country which hugged his territory - country that was now rose-daubed and splashed gold with groves of elegant musasas in bloom, the tranquil colours of late afternoon just adding their tinge as he crossed back into familiar tracts.

It was but a while after this - at least a good full moon later when Umbulala was fully recovered to health - that the cat embarked on a reconnaissance of his territory. Long overdue, it as likely evolved from a need as much metaphysical, as physical. It was also to spotlight an episode in his life which would alter it forever. He was generally roving about the bush at the time, nosing at everything worthy of attention in that infinitely discreet way cats use to masterly effect. With his ears and eyes primed, a slight, desultory movement ahead of him, just beyond a tangle of trees and scrub, drew his attention. Not immediately recognizable, it aroused something of that extravagant felid curiosity which can be the boon, or bane of a cat's life.

He moved deliberately towards it; slowly at first, his head held low, the steps softly resilient in their velvet-cushioned tread. With every chance of it being buffalo ahead, even the rare possibility of lion - neither prospect of which thrilled him - the need for stealth was paramount. So was maintaining a safe distance. He continued on, senses locked on the spot. A few cautionary steps more: then silence, abrupt and fathomless gripped the jungle, momentarily catching its breath as it echoed in a deep, staccato grunt

that sounded fire across the lull, and
set the fur ranged along Umbulala's
tensed, firm back bristling myriad
exclamations!

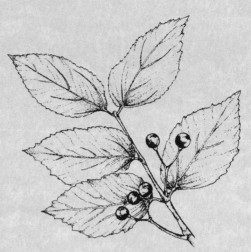

He stopped dead in his tracks, the
thought that the bush in its quietude
might also be deciphering the sound
flashing through his mind. But the
panther knew better than that.
Every bird and animal thereabouts, without distinction, would have
recognized a major predator the instant it spoke, thus setting in motion the
unabashed cacophony of honks and coughs and screechs that invariably
follows. It is the wild belling in alarm, with every creature alerted, crying
out a warning. Hence the reason why cats are such silent movers. And hence
that suddcn, peremptory hush beforehand.....like the lull before the storm.

There was leopard up ahead - not buffalo, nor lion, or some lesser animal
with a predilection for being hunted rather than hunting. The moment
Umbulala heard that harsh, coughing *grunt-ha...grunt-ha* all doubts of his
own fallibility dissolved. He quickened his pace, taking full advantage of
his colour to avoid being spotted. Barracking, black-faced vervet monkeys
were already weaving a maze of hysteria in and around the choked network
of branches and foliage over where the errant leopard lay hidden. From every
other quarter of the surrounding bush, protest upon protest erupted to add to
the wild uproar of alarm which had predictably followed the initial predatory
silence; a silence best described as "danger's overture", when neither bird
nor insect trills its song.

Quietly as evening mist, the panther slipped from shadow to shadow. Once
in striking distance, he flew at the flimsy barricade of green shielding the
intruder, smashing through its defences and straight onto the other cat in one
swoop. Over and over they rolled in embrace, leaves and bits of branch and

twig flying in every direction. Although smaller, the intruder was agile, matching Umbulala stroke for stroke. They tumbled apart. In an instant the panther was up and onto his haunches, about to parry with his favourite bite to the throat.........when something about his opponent's posture promptly brought him up short.

The newcomer was lying invitingly on its back, paws in the air, its neck and throat clearly exposed. It was an obvious sign of submission, but it took Umbulala utterly by surprise, quite undermining his reserve! He blinked a moment, not entirely sure what to do. Then, with the same caution that always served him well in awkward situations, he sidled closer and sniffed at the prostrate cat; gingerly at first. The experience was not unpleasant. He continued on in this vein until, for some inexplicable reason quite beyond his ken, a gentle fluttering motion started up inside him - like a moth shyly playing about his face. Mother had never prepared him for this! And all of a sudden he felt gauche and thick-limbed; a sensation he'd thought he'd left behind with cubhood.

As for the other cat, a fine young female lying flat on the ground with her head thrown back enticingly, she appeared blissfully ignorant of her assailant's confusion. What was particularly noteworthy about her was that she was just coming into season; a fact which would have automatically explained her behaviour to any swain less green than Umbulala on matters of the heart. But those wild oats about which much is made were, as yet, little more than bits of grass to Umbulala.

"I'll play for time....pretend I'm angry",
he told himself, desperately trying to get some order into his razzled thoughts.

He fell to nudging her with his snout in that characteristic way cats adopt in these circumstances, his manner gruff for effect. But not for long. His self-control began to waver ruthlessly, misty notions playing about his senses as he noted with a pang how lovely she was; and once again he had to grapple with himself to regain his composure. To lose control, if that's what was

happening to him, simply wouldn't do for a cat of his tenor; of this he was certain! It required thinking about. He appeared to leave.

The smaller cat, sensing his agitation, rolled onto her side......then slowly began to rise on all fours with studied care, lest she antagonise the magnificent panther further She was just about up when, out of the blue Umbulala turned, and in a lightning stroke that caught her off guard, bowled her over! She was by no means felled by it and responded instantly to the challenge. Throwing herself across the ground with the thrust of it, she rolled over a couple of times before springing up to face the panther. Once, twice - three times he challenged her in like fashion; and each time she responded without flinching.

Considering she couldn't be sure just how much of it was bluff and how much genuine, her resolve was astounding, lighter of build as she was; and Umbulala suspected that any other bitch leopard would have run for her life by now. But not this little beauty!

"Ooooohhh - what a mate she would make!"
his thoughts veritably sang as he dashed up the bole of a mighty fig tree linking arms with another, thence out onto a stout branch; glancing back over his shoulder in her direction, his mouth dropped open in a conspiratorial grin.

Quicker than thought she was off after him, and Umbulala noted her every movement with the eye of one who appreciates nature's tapestry. Her large eyes, golden bright as a daisy's heart, sparkled with fire; indeed she did seem to the panther the very essence of vitality and beauty captured breathless in one radiant life-form.

She was only a little way behind when Umbulala scurried along the branch, sprang to the next tree,

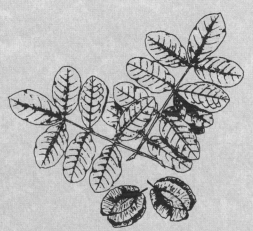

thence down to the ground again and away on a mad whirligig of darts and dashes round the bush. As if swallow-winged he skimmed and skittered about at mercurial speed - yet all the while the little spotted leopard kept but a few paces behind him. Occasionally, if a change of tempo seemed in order, he'd wheel around abruptly and catch her a gentle pat on the rump; at which she'd promptly move to cuff him back with a dramatic flourish, or just make a show of tumbling over. Not to reciprocate in some way would have spoilt the game.

On and on they frolicked like a pair of defenceless cubs, oblivious to time's trawl. Only later, in the shade of a copse on the water's edge, under a figured canopy of foliage through which sunlight flowed, dappled and ribboned to weave honied braids along her back, did the enchanting stranger declare her mind to Umbulala for the first time:

"It was claimed by the birds of the air......"
she began beguilingly,

"that here in this part of the jungle there lived, all alone, a mighty black leopard by name of Umbulala to whom Mother nature had given the strength of a lion, the wisdom of the eagle owl and the cunning of the mamba, deadliest of snakes. Why, it was alleged, that like the mamba he could so hypnotize his victims with just a stare they would stand petrified in fear! I could not believe them; and then when Brother swallow announced to me that you were virtually the size of a lioness, I cried that such a thing was impossible! So I came to see for myself, travelling far, and for many moons, and always

following the river. And the nearer I approached, the greater did the tales become. Ah.......but how foolish I feel, for now I see that you are all these things, and I can only marvel at the wit of Mother nature!"
Emitting a purr as mellow and resonant as the drumming of a distant waterfall, she rubbed her prettily stippled head against Umbulala's, like

polished ebony in comparison - so stark was the contrast - and nearly twice as big.

She was called Tola, so whispered the wind, and reminded Umbulala - who had been a solitary cat for more moons now than he cared to remember - of his days as a cub, especially in the way she would dash mock assaults on him just like Kusasa; so vibrantly alive and quite fearless, qualities he cherished above all others. And so, over dewy dawns and sun-washed days, and nights that effervesced with stars, they spent many moments together, breaking only from their revels to hunt when hunger demanded.

Naturally the relationship didn't go unnoticed. Indeed, there were those who went so far as to declaim it a scandal. Like the supercilious lourie - the go-away bird - overheard from its perch in a fig tree effusing as much to a parrot; the patent disinterest of the latter abundantly apparent as it busied itself with a loose feather that had been sorely irritating it.

"It's a disgrace I tell you...."

the lourie jabbered on, unperturbed by the other's indifference,

"the way those two fool around like a pair of otters! You'd think one as feared as Umbulala would behave with more decorum?!"

"Whyyyy???"

the parrot teasingly retorted, suddenly unable to resist a gibe at the busybody bird.

"Well....!!"

the lourie tetchily exclaimed in reply, scratching its head and searching its pea-brain for an answer. Clearly put out by the parrot's manner, it hopped up and down agitatedly; then, never one not to have the last word, flew off in a clumsy flurry of feathers with the resounding burst:

"G..'waaay! G..'waaay!!"

to find a more agreeable ear elsewhere.

But a final retort from the parrot put the seal on the matter:

"If *you* were Umbulala you wouldn't give a hoot!"

With the arrival of the tropic winds bringing the long awaited storms of another rainy season, the thirsty land began to breathe again. From sunrise to sunset, for days following days the life-giving deluge drummed down its wealth, showering soothing draughts of refreshment across tracts hitherto parched and gasping. Water seeped into every crack and crevice of the hot ground, sending drifts of steam wafting heavenward........as if Mother earth was visibly sighing in relief!

Small creeks that had just been dry, sandy beds came down in spate; while the river, previously reduced to little more than a stream well below its usual flow, with mold and moss wreathing its margins, swelled again in seasonal transformation to mighty watercourse, lapping murky brown from bank to bank.

Mid the surge and thrust of all this richness, the jungle was literally painted anew. Where greens bedecked greens, and reds and purples and yellows elsewhere, the colours of nature shimmered with a luminescence so fresh and ethereal, it was indefinable. Later, when the first flush of the *wet* had ebbed, there hung above the dank splash and fragrance the infinite sounds of the wild, like the votive notes of a song raised in celebration; a paean that rang the atmosphere clean in the joyous rasp of animal and insect, and the infinite timbre of birdsong. Even the hippos added their thrum as they lazily snorted and wallowed in river traces silt-hued and brimming again.

This was the time of birth when most animals drop their young; a time of plenty, of good hunting, and gradually as the season progressed, of renewal: a unique panorama played out at every level, and unsurpassed by anything else in nature. A remarkable pendulum of alternatives, it swung continuously

between freshness and staleness, the budding of new unions, the demise of old, birth and death - with every living thing an essential component of the whole. Throughout it all, Umbulala and Tola remained together, an inseparable pair: spotted leopard, black panther.

While leopards in the tropics may mate and breed all year round, the passing of the *wet* marks the demise of the calving season for most other animals. So when, some moons after the last rains, Tola found herself to be in cub, the whole cyclic phenomena of life making life continued on apace, as if never having stopped. For Tola it would be her first birth, and as the dawns leading up to it fell away, and the crisp freshness in the air increased with the retreat of the *wet* and the steady advance of the *dry*, Umbulala led her up to the crest of the long kopje and to the cave that had served him well during his recovery from the python's attack. Here he urged her to stay to take advantage of its snug seclusion as a den, while he took responsibility for providing food for all her needs.

"Worry not little one",
he murmured, rubbing his head against her.

"Mother nature is with you, for are not all the young her cubs?" Reluctantly, she agreed to remain behind; but only after some coaxing from Umbulala. The notion of being parted from him for any length of time had never figured in her thoughts; not consciously anyway. And as he took his leave of her, she watched wistfully, suddenly aware that reality had caught up with fantasy.

The colours of the day waved in the sunlight as Umbulala descended the kopje. On reaching the lower slopes, he stopped to look up over his shoulder in the direction of the den, conveniently hidden from sight amid the uppermost crags of the kopje, and where Tola would remain until after the birth of her young. As he stood there, burnished bronze in the harsh beat of the sun, one caught the faintest glimmer of rosettes, the distinctive pattern of the spotted cousin still present in leopards of Umbulala's mien, as if it were their other self - the primitive spirit inherent in all creatures.

Turning to continue down the kopje, his attention rested a moment on a sight new to the slopes since last he was there. Like a host of tiny trumpets blazing out in bands of colour, garlands of morning glories were twisting and twining around shrubs and grasses: yellow ones, some as white as cloud, others quivering and bobbing bright in the clear air like the chests of myriad lilac-breasted rollers. Further back up the slopes, the everlastings in their multitude were blooming anew.

CROWN OF HORNS

Cat's eyes look to another plain!

Umbulala sighed lightly, a mild sense of wonder in his tone. Slipping casually through the forest underbrush, he'd glanced above him, a precaution that had become a habit, and had been immediately struck by what he saw there. It was a sight not entirely unfamiliar, yet one he'd never fully appreciated before, like so much else about Mother nature's craft. Perhaps it was the wood-for-the-trees syndrome; who knows. But he really noticed, as never before, the forest canopy in all its intricate detail, and how different it appeared from underneath looking up at it, to when one looked across the top of it from the high country.

Then, as always, it resembled a gently rolling lagoon, with swells of green slowly rising and falling with the breeze. But now! Umbulala sucked in his breath. It was vastly different. Like the horns of numerous impala antelopes locked in combat, the branches of the tree tops were clasped and crossed every which way, chiselling out trembling patterns against the interminable blue of the sky, and setting the sunlight to jig and dart through the array of foliage in shimmering reflections that dazzled the eye.

As the wind scurried overhead in and out the leaves, and monkeys and birds played about in the upper branches, dew fell like rain on the web of plantlife below, beckoning what flowers that grew there to strain upward to the sun.

Stepping lightly through a clearing, Umbulala shook the dampness from his coat, and for a brief moment amused himself with the madcap notion that shaking his fur until it stood on end must be a bit like Brother porcupine shooting his quills perpendicular! So he supposed.

While his thoughts played about thus, his ears, ever primed, picked up a sound on the wind. Although only slight, the cat instinctively froze in his tracks. Focusing his hearing right in, he slowly moved his head round, sifting every nuance until he was near enough sure of the source of the sound, and its approximate distance away. The superlative, glassy-eyed stare of the stalker took over. Analysing every play of light, the cold eyes rifled through a welter of wood and green to hone in on something toward the river - just two black points amid the choking clutch of vegetation skirting the water's edge.

It was the apex of a pair of horns. Immediately positioning himself downwind of it, he stared hard at the spot. They belonged to a large antelope. Identifying it was the difficulty. What with the distance, and the obstructions of trees and bushes between distorting and playing havoc with his vision, that was no easy task. Time dragged involuntarily. The horn tips began to take on a shape; the shape of a wishbone, it looked to be from where Umbulala stood intently concentrating his gaze. Waterbuck? He wondered. And

if waterbuck, had its fine senses drawn a bead on him!

He continued to stare hard at the spot, keen eyesight filtering through the haze of reeds and foliage strung between like a wattled web of camouflage. The ability of the cat's eyes to decipher shapes within shapes is phenomenal. With what can only be described as almost supernatural vision, they appear able to probe and penetrate to the very core of the scenë under observation. Hence, even as Umbulala scrutinized the dank bush ahead, the framework of vegetation was magnifying and transforming before his eyes. The cat's excellent zoom vision condensed and amplified to draw out the shape of the animal that lay hidden, just beyond the immediate cover of branch and greenery; cover which hung like an illusory veil calculated to baffle even the sharpest eye.

An outline began to grow beneath the horns. Fuzzy grey in character, it took on a head. It was soft muzzled and doe-eyed. The head in turn melded to a strong neck and shoulders. Finally, white bearded and shaggy collared, the pristine shape of a bull waterbuck came full into view. Standing motionless in the greenery, its large fig leaf ears were spread wide to catch every murmur.

The waterbuck antelope is neither flamboyant nor glamourous: its beauty is otherwise. Like a line of music finely drawn, or a lotus blossom at the peak of perfection, the beauty of the waterbuck is precise and refined; of a classical quality so much its own, the animal is unmistakeable. Presently, to confirm it, Umbulala whiffed the distinctive musky odour of waterbuck on a gust of wind out of that direction.

The panther crouched flat, an ebony wraith on powerful limbs, his lithe tail curved for balance. He oozed forward as close as possible to the ground, his belly just brushing the stubble. With its covering of fur being softer and thicker than elsewhere on the cat's body, and thus muffling any sound, the cat glided in liquid motion along the dappled ground like a swallow over water.

The buck blinked in its hide of green. Swinging an elegant head around, it scratched its white-ellipsed rump with a sweep of a horn, before returning to browse on some tender shoots of a young ebony tree growing to one side. Something wasn't right however; it could sense it. Umbulala was now considerably closer, although still downwind in a stiff breeze. But the waterbuck was clearly uneasy. Every so often it would break from browsing, and its handsome head would reappear above the lush greenery; ears and nostrils feverishly twitching, its eyes flickering across the surrounding bush, alert to the slightest sense of danger.

And sense danger it could; every hair of its shaggy hide said so, raised like myriad antennae receiving information not conceivably carried to it on a breeze blowing the opposite way! By some uncanny sixth sense the waterbuck could detect a lingering threat in the near vicinity that was not readily identifiable - yet it could neither have seen Umbulala, nor heard nor smelt him, the panther having been well downwind of the buck the whole time.

One of the more absorbing mysteries of nature is this extra-sensory perception seemingly present in animals of all types. It is a perception which, without the apparent aid of any of the animal's major senses, or the wind, is capable of alerting a creature to some alien presence it believes might pose a threat to it; of leading back together from entirely different directions a lost fawn and its mother; or two mates separated by distance, each well out of earshot or scent of the other.

The old bull waterbuck was a seasoned survivor, in whose mind Brother error had little chance of working mischief. Well practised in the ways of defence, the buck, when it looked to be standing motionless, was actually slowly manoeuvring itself backward into the benign stretch of river behind it, so to face head on the danger that lurked before it in the bushes - confident in its ability to stave off any threat with a set of stout and formidable horns.

So coincidence it may have been. But when Umbulala, irritated at his failure to obtain some tender food in the night, had peered straight at the waterbuck but moments prior to his breaking cover, the wily buck, by some uncanny quirk, had simultaneously focused on the crouching black form in amongst the vegetation. Instantly, instead of bolting for its life, it had retreated rearwards into the river.

Standing foursquare, with the water lapping its stomach, the buck straightaway presented Umbulala with an ultimatum - fall back, or cross a wallow of thick, sticky mud which would only retard the cat's progress; thence the same distance again through haunches high water where the courageous buck, holding its ground and looking to be in full charge of the position, had the advantage.

Waterbuck are adept swimmers; they are also exceedingly proficient at employing water as a secure means of refuge. Umbulala rushed forward, a bluff charge to unnerve his quarry and so flush it from its stronghold. But the buck stood steadfast. In two bounds the panther was at the edge of the bank; in another four he could have been on the bull - if he didn't fall foul of the mud. The chances of him avoiding that happening were small. And in the face of horns primed ready and waiting, and which would give no quarter, he wasn't about to risk it. Like the waterbuck, the panther also bore that especial gift of instinct Mother nature bestows in abundance on those with the care and know-how to use it. With the mud, thence the water to hinder him, he was at a disadvantage from the start; and Umbulala wasn't one to rush in impetuously like some feckless young cat. He hadn't forgotten the lesson of the sable.

And so, aware of the trap that lay ahead, the panther stopped short of the mud. Held at the water's edge, his only recourse was to hiss and snarl ineffectually at the waterbuck, more out of frustration than anger; just those matchless fangs, reflecting sharp-white in the light, hinting at the clout they might have administered.

Stalemate ensued. The proud waterbuck flared its nostrils wide, no intention of letting slip its advantage. Graceful and majestic in defiance, only the eyes - rightfully soft and genial, now bloodshot and burning - betrayed the same audacious spirit that during the rutting season had set it to repel the challenges of the stout young bulls, would-be usurpers of its dominance. A monarch in all its prime, here indeed was a match for the cat exalted above all others.

Not a bird trilled as the two animals stared at one another across an abyss of stillness that stood like a conspiracy between. Finally the waterbuck broke the deadlock:

"Not yet, hunter of the dark - not yet!"

it hoarsely cried across at the cat.

"But when my time comes, I pray that you are the one to deliver that final death stroke - and not those whelps that run with their tails between their legs, and wrench off hunks of the still-living flesh before the very eyes of those that flee them!"

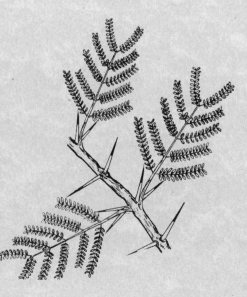

Umbulala coughed. It was a low, guttural snipe of irritation. He'd met his match, as well he knew. There could be only one response - buck and panther should go their separate ways.

The big cat swung off along the river margin, its lush skirting of trees and scrub sweeping him from sight as slickly as sand glissading down a slope. He'd met his match alright, and Brother wind whipping through the reeds exhorted him to remember as much:

"Vanity is nothing....."
hushed tones seemed to extol,

"wisdom all!"
Umbulala sighed. There were times when, quite honestly, he could do without the reflective intimations of Brother wind! Yet he supposed it was a good thing hearing the truth for what it was. Anyway, he'd heard tell that the waterbuck's coarse hide made it unappetising eating - although how much trust he could place in such a rumour he didn't much know. Doubtless time and experience would tell.

With such thoughts and questions playing about his mind, Umbulala hastened on and out of the river valley. Already the heat and humidity were beginning to cloy the day. He hadn't yet made a kill, and time was pressing.

BEYOND THE CIRCLE

There are mountains....
hills and valleys ahead

Sunset flushed magenta over the treetops, stencilling lacy patterns against a blue of evening sky washed gold in the afterglow. A swell of rosy hued brilliance, it lifted over the jungle like waves of carmine bee-eaters, rippling a garland around the coming twilight. Umbulala surveyed the splendid diorama of close of day with the eye of one never wanting of wonder. He loved this moment just prior to dusk.

With all four legs indolently dangling, he lay at ease in that seeming half-sleep of cats along the sloping trunk of a favourite tree he kept for when the shadows lengthened; a lovely, yellow thorn acacia, or fever tree, which grew at an incongruous angle out the side of a cliff face, and as such afforded the big cat a perfect panoramic view of the whole spectacle of afternoon melding to evening. Harbinger of a dreamtime made not for dreams, there was in the abstract beauty of this time of day a quality of contradiction that never failed to excite him. When the jungle seemed ready for sleep it was only just awakening; all appeared still, yet was not. In its breathlessness life almost seemed to be marking time.

Umbulala remembered his lovely mate and the strangeness of the moment dawning upon her. Now, in the warm glow of sunset, as he raked the bark with his claws until it bled, before sweeping down into the jungle to hunt,

the panther's mind wandered to thoughts of his own life as a cub - the warmth and unflagging spirit of his mother, the awesome might of his father - memories suffused with a richness of melange as abiding as the seasons.

He hadn't long left his vantage point in the fever tree when with that crude indifference the present treats the past, something unexpected brought Umbulala hurtling back to reality. From out of nowhere a whiff of wind, warning of immediate danger, tingled his nostrils, stopping him dead in his tracks. Daydreaming had set a snare to catch him out again! Umbulala had inadvertently wandered into a pack of wild dog! It was not a wholly pleasant situation for any leopard, however big and fearsome; and Umbulala cursed the enfeebling emotions that had disarmed his senses and landed him there:

"Away with you Brother error!",

his thoughts screamed,

"where your dread trawl sweeps, havoc and ruin are close behind!"
Two brindled dogs detached themselves from the body of the pack and rounded up behind the panther, completing a circle.

Umbulala raised not a hair of his hide; nor flattened his ears against his head. He knew he mustn't show a trace of emotion - even though his palpitating heart was doing a lively rendition of the dance of the cranes! The panther's mind raced: he had to distract the attention of the dogs just long enough to enable him to thwart an attack. Mid a ragbag of thoughts the germ of an idea took hold, and

Umbulala, with all the wit of one bent on circumventing his own perdition, saw its promise immediately. He addressed the pack, his sharp feline finesse coming full into play:

> "I have spent since the first quarter of the moon searching, when time permitted, for the four-toed dogs. As is well known in the jungle, I, Umbulala, seek all kinds of knowledge and wisdom. Thus I would like to know what is the favourite food of this dog pack that hunts anything and everything with the will to move?!"

And pulling his long tail around him, the panther crouched.

Piercing eyes gazed straight at the first dog, now looking askance at Umbulala - not a little dumbfounded by the panther's behaviour! After a momentary silence, palpable with expectation, she replied, her wiry, tortoiseshell frame quivering with excitement at the prospect ahead:

> "Umbulala! There is none so brave as one who will boldly walk up to us and expect to live! You are an exceptional animal. As to your query - of what possible need could knowing the favourite food of we humble dogs be to a hunter as famed and feared as you?!!"

There was a pause. Already the pack had relaxed its guard, a sense of feeling secure in numbers having taken hold. Two dogs took to scratching themselves languidly, one under the chin, the other behind an ear. Umbulala fancied he could easily snap the neck of the one closest in the wink of an owl's eye......but Mother nature stayed the impulse. Instead he replied:

> "As all in the jungle are aware, I, Umbulala, have claimed this area as my territory. But I wish to rid it of the dog pack. So, when I know what is the wild dog's favourite food, I shall destroy it all - and run you from my domain!!"

At this, an uproarious round of mirth erupted from the six strong pack. Sniggering smugly at the nerve of the panther, the dominant dog burst back with a confident retort:

"I do believe the fool is serious! And
he is even brazen enough to expect an
answer!"
That might have been the end it. It wasn't.
Umbulala's wily ruse was having good its
effect. With a showy flourish of her
outsize ears, the dog cried out dramatically,
affecting a tone ostentatious in its mockery:

"But wait! There's no hurry; you're
not going anyway black cat! Seeing
you are so desperate for an answer, let's not disappoint you. You are after
discovering - *mighty* Umbulala - what the favourite food of we dogs
might be - we *humble* hounds, lighter of build as we are than even the
smallest leopard! What say you to it being crocodile.....or perhaps, hee,
hee....rhino... or.....or better still, the biggest of all, ELEPHANT!! There
Umbulala....ha haaa!! What say you to that, eh? Hee heee! HAA
haaaaa!!"
The throng of dogs arrayed around her were nearly hysterical with glee, each
one barely able to contain itself as the pack leader yowled and chortled on;
brimming with that brash brand of confidence that is the agitator's mark.

"And what's Umbulala's favourite food then - perhaps we the dog pack
will destroy them and run YOU out, hmmmmm?!"
The taunt had scarcely cut the air before the harsh, sawing roar of leopard
was resounding back over echoes of cracking bones and tearing flesh,
distilling it in one:

"Dogs! DOGS!! Yes...doogggggs are a leopard's favourite food!!"
With barely a chance for any to know quite what was happening, the scene
had erupted into a gruesome tableau vivant. Deadly claws slashed havoc and
disarray into the pack, catching it completely by surprise - and leaving two
dead and two more in the grips of the panther in the space of moments.

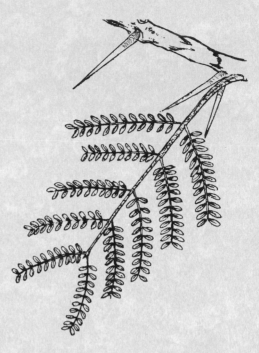

Taking one look at the carnage erupting around her, the dominant dog bolted for her life in a pall of dust. Soon outdistancing the panther when he made to follow her upon finishing off the dogs in his clutches, she dodged around a clutch of thornbush and away; her one surviving pack mate limping after her in frantic pursuit. Umbulala stopped short. Four wild dogs down, and one mauled in a twinkling took some doing; even for as big and tough a cat as he.

He was still thinking along these lines, with barely time to regain his breath, when one of the dogs that had fled, suddenly came hurtling back through the air - clean over the top of the thorn scrub it had just that moment disappeared around! A pathetic whine accompanied its flight as mid a surge of air exuding from its lungs, it crashed down with a merciless thud onto the hard ground........right at the feet of one decidedly flabbergasted Umbulala! His misery of curiosity was quickly allayed. Less than an instant later, careening through the encrusted phalanx of quill sharp thornbush like it was a mere froth of fern, a bull buffalo broke cover.

Whuffing and blowing steam, it galumphed over to the dog and promptly proceeded to gore the wretched animal into oblivion - massive, hooked horns and machete-edged hooves working it over like vultures on a corpse. Only when it had rolled its great, cumbrous weight over and over the cadaver, again and again, was the bull content the dog was decidedly dead. Finally, lifting a ponderous, forked head foaming and bloody with the testimony of the deed, the big bull turned toward the panther, crouched peering wide-eyed in the buffalo's direction.

"Tis strange to fight on your side......."

the bull declared huskily to the watchful cat,

"but one couldn't ask Mother nature for a finer ally."

Umbulala shrugged, glancing from the buffalo to the wild dog - what was discernible of it - and back again to the buffalo.

"It's a pity Inyati...."

the cat chuckled to the big bull,

"that Mother nature never kept these hounds to herself! They used to be pets of hers, you know; that's why they carry the colours of all the animals on their hide. One day, so the legend goes, she went to feed them - and one bit her! So cross was Mother nature, she promptly picked the ingrate up by its ears, and swinging it round and round, cast it down to earth! Hence those ridiculous, lily pad ears they bear to this day!!"

Inyati snorted and grunted delightedly, appreciating the tale. Wheeling round, the big beast lumbered back the way it had come - *around* the thornbush this time, not through it - leaving the spoils for whom nature rightfully intended them.

Umbulala remained awhile where he was, squatted on the ground in a half-crouch, caution his mentor. He still had to be careful, lest hyaena came shuffling too near. Casting a quick glance around him, he rose. Hastening over to a wild dog carcass, he gripped it firmly - then made straight for the nearest tree that looked like it would make a suitable larder in the short-term. That done, he wasted little time retracing his steps.

Checking the way was still clear, he gripped hold of a second carcass by the neck, straddled the body with his forelegs and began to drag it away - this time to the cave in the long bronzed kopje where Tola awaited the birth of her cubs. Although the carcass was awkward and impeded him a little as he climbed, the big cat made steady progress. And even as he neared the den, a host of jackals was already ringing a silvery message around the skies, which carried on the wind to the far corners of the jungle proclaiming the news that the dog pack was no more: put to rout by Umbulala that very day. And thus was Umbulala's place in jungle folklore assured.

Tola met him outside the den and stayed just long enough to eat her fill. The pains of the impending birth were now coming sharp and fast, warning her back to the comfort of the cave to await the arrival of her cubs, now simply a matter of time away. Umbulala's only move was to watch her go, following her traces with a low, purring "aaooommm" that spoke volumes.

Tola tilted her head in his direction, having felt that chill stare boring through her skull almost to her soul. For a brief moment she remained there, in front of the den, looking toward the big panther, sire of her cubs, as if drawing in the vibes of some urgent message meant only for her. Then, with a quick, upward tilt of her snout in acknowledgement, so characteristic of cats, she turned at last into the cave, content in believing that while her panther kept guard, none would enter her sanctum.

All through that night Umbulala lay at the entrance to the den, watching the moon on its chartered course across the sky, and listening to the infinite sounds of jungle life going on apace - each skirling out a tale to the dark. The distant drum of lion beating out the wild's own distinctive reveille; hyaena on the kill, whooping and chortling their primal chorus across the stygian depths and reminding all of death's inevitable tread; a civet, secretive and sylph-like, snuffling out prey on the kopje's slopes; while from out of the blackened panoply of anonymous vegetation hugging its base, the macabre lament of a tree hyrax rattling and wailing to a crescendo.

Umbulala even thought he heard Brother wind, boon companion to many an animal, whispering wistfully over the time-honoured terraces of the kopje, and in and out the tentacled branches of the trees, swaying like eerie shadows of themselves in the night air:

"Take note - *he who eats the hearts of lions*, and smites the dogs of havoc! Nature has come full circle."

Umbulala knew better. It was only just beginning.

REFERENCES TO BLACK
LEOPARD IN AFRICA

Black leopards are melanistic mutations of the common spotted leopard *Panthera pardus*. More commonly associated with Asia, black leopards also appear in Africa, but to a lesser degree.

Dyer, A./Kuhn, B., *Classic African Animals: The Big Five (*Winchester Press, New York 1973)

Guggisberg, C. A. W., *Wild Cats of the World* (David & Charles, 1975)

Gunther, A., *Proceedings Zoological Society London*, pp. 243-5 (3 March 1885)

Gunther, A., *Proceedings Zoological Society London*, pp. 203-5 (6 April 1886)

Maberly, C.T. Astley, *Animals of East Africa* (Howard Timmins, Cape Town 1960)

Pocock, R. I., *The Field*, Vol 148, p. 707 (21 October 1926)

Pocock, R. I., *Proceedings Zoological Society London*, pp. 543-91 (1932)

Roberts, A., *The mammals of South Africa* (Trustees of the "Mammals of South Africa" Book Fund, Johannesburg 1951)

Schouteden, H., *Ann. Mus Congo Belge.*, Ser II, Vol III, pp. 169-332 (1945)

Sclater, W. L., *The mammals of South Africa*, Vol I (R.H. Porter, London 1900)

Shuker, K. P. N., *Mystery Cats of the World* (Robert Hale, London 1989)

ILLUSTRATIONS

FULL-PAGE LINE & PEN DRAWINGS

Leopard	X	Bush scenic	102
Bushpig	6	Sable antelope	107
Gemsbok, or oryx	13	Bullfrog	116
Spotted hyaena	16	Black leopard (panther)	122
Black rhinoceros	22	Fish eagle	124
Zebra	29	Black leopard (panther)	131
Helmeted/Crowned guinea-fowl	33	Eagle owl	136
Nile crocodile	38	Egyptian geese	140
Giraffe	43	Black leopard (panther)	146
Impala ram	49	Impala doe and fawn	151
Cock ostrich	52	Water monitor lizard, or leguaan	154
Lion	57	Lioness	159
Wildebeest	63	Elephant	165
Genet	66	Duiker doe and fawn	171
Elephant	72	Black leopard (panther)	178
Spider web	76	Black leopard (panther)	184
Lioness	79	Waterbuck bull	187
Caracal, or African lynx	85	Cape buffalo bull	196
Waterbuck bull	92	Wild dog, or African hunting dog	200
Leopard	94	Black leopard (panther)	209

COLOUR PLATES

Burchell's zebra	3	Lion	110
Bush scenic	9	Umbulala	113
Fungi-sprouting elephant dung	18	Impala	119
Ingwe & cubs	25	Hippopotamus	126
Black-headed oriole	36	Bush scenic	143
Bushbuck	41	Umbulala	149
Steenbok	46	Umbulala	156
Baobab	54	Scarab beetle dung balls	161
Impala	60	Umbulala	163
Greater kudu	69	Elephant herd	167
Umbulala	74	Umbulala	174
Wildebeest	82	Brown-headed parrot	181
Locust	88	Waterbuck bull	190
Chacma baboon	96	Goliath heron	198
Umbulala	99	Umbulala	203

GLOSSARY

Aloes

Flowering succulents of the lily family numbering around 200 species native to Africa and ranging from dwarf forms to trees up to 15m tall. The juice of some is used in medicine.

Antbear hole

A large burrow dug in the side of a termitarium by the aardvark: aka the antbear - an unmistakeable pig-like animal with an elongated snout and powerful claws which feeds mainly on termites and ants. Some antbear holes have a network of galleries with as many as 25 openings. Abandoned burrows are often appropriated by reptiles, bats, honey badgers, owls, warthogs; even hyaenas and jackals.

Antelope

Cud-chewing, grazing or browsing mammals. Antelopes predominantly occur in Africa, and differ significantly from deer in that their single-pointed horns, encased by a horny sheath, are not shed; and can form rings as evidence of age as they grow.

Ant-heap

General bush term in Africa for a mound or hill formed by a colony of termites - flying "white ants" - living in an organised community. While a termitarium may reach up to 3m in height, many can exceed this. Ant-heaps that become "deserted cities" may have trees up to 100 years old growing out of them.

Antlion

Antlions, or rather their larvae, lie buried in ambush at the bottom of funnel-shaped sand pitfalls they dig up to 5cm deep. With only pincer-like jaws projecting they seize any ant or small insect which happens to slip down the slope! After a period of growth the larva spins a cocoon in the ground; the winged adult which emerges is not unlike an ungainly dragonfly.

Bushpig

Omnivorous, with long, bristly coats and tufted ears, bushpigs, or *Red River Hogs*, range widely over Africa. They are good swimmers and are considered by some to be more intelligent than many dogs. When adult they're formidable adversaries, with a fully grown pig weighing over 90kg.

Calabash pod

Of the gourd family which includes edible fruits - viz watermelon, cucumber or squash - and hard-shelled ornamental or inedible gourds (such as the bottle gourd). The latter are commonly used as cooking utensils and vessels when hollowed out.

Canines

The four large conical, dagger-like teeth on each side of the top and bottom jaws of the carnivores. Canines in the cats are more sharply pointed than in the hyaenas, for example, where they are used not only for killing, but for crushing and grinding bones.

Caracal

The so-called "African lynx". A fiery-coated, tuft-eared cat grouped among the smaller felids, caracals are solitary characters with a remarkable ability to catch birds on the wing. Due to this agility they were at one time trained to catch hares and feathered game.

Civet

The black and grey African civet, often miscalled "civet cat" and largest of the viverrids, is a long-bodied, long-legged carnivore with scent glands used for marking (and perfume manufacture by man). It's solitary and nocturnal with a "masked" face giving it the appearance of a Victorian burglar. Smaller and more weasel-like, the *Tree civet* and rare fish-eating *Aquatic civet* are also recognised.

Combretum

Plants numbering numerous tropical and sub-tropical trees and shrubs typically found with hard tough wood, and distinctive, papery four-winged fruit. Scented flowers grow in spikes or catkins, while trees with rounded, shady crowns can grow to about 8m.

Cream-of-tartar pod

The large, edible gourdlike fruit of the baobab, so-called "cream-of-tartar" from the agreeably biting taste of the floury pulp inside its hard, woody shell. Popular with elephants and baboons - hence *monkey bread* - the velvety, grey-green pods make adequate cups; even water bailers. Baobabs live for hundreds of years and can reach great size: up to 20m tall and some 15m or more around the trunk. Smaller varieties occur in Australia and Madagascar.

Den

A temporary dwelling or lair of a wild animal - especially a beast of prey - in a cave, under fallen trees, deep in thick scrub, a large antbear hole, or even in thick elephant grass that can reach over 4m in height. In all cases well hidden, difficult to approach, and defendable.

Dew claw

The claw that terminates the fifth toe pad not reaching to the ground on the forepaw of a felid. This fifth claw, which corresponds to the thumbnail in humans, is much relied upon in climbing and in holding prey, and can inflict deadly damage in an attack.

Euphorbias

Among the specimens of euphorbia, of which there are several, is the candelabrum tree, so-called because the erect stance of its four-angled branches makes it resemble a multi-pointed candlestick. Euphorbias are found mainly on rocky kopjes, and can grow up to 9m or more in height.

Fever mosquitoes

Mosquitoes that transmit *malaria* (and the most frequently fatal variety **blackwater fever**) and *jungle yellow fever*.

Fever tree

The handsome yellow thorn, or yellow barked acacia tree. Found mainly along watercourses, the name "fever tree" derives from early days of colonisation when it was erroneously associated with malaria. Where yellow barked acacias thrived, so also did malaria mosquitoes!

Francolin

The so-called "quail of Africa". Any of several species of popular African game birds, francolins are typically chestnut and tawny in colour, with drooping hindquarters not unlike the larger guinea-fowl.

Galagos

Very active lower primates - aka *Bushbabies* and *Night apes* - galagos are arboreal and mostly nocturnal, with big ears, huge eyes adapted to night vision, elongated hind-limbs, a soft woolly coat and long, often bushy tail. Confined to forests and woodlands, they move very fast through the trees, leaping frog-fashion. Among their calls is one like a child crying in distress - hence the name Bushbaby.

Herd Matriarch

Normally the oldest cow elephant with a group of related elephant cows and their young. She determines stability and ranging patterns for the family unit which might include sisters and adolescent bulls.

Kopje

A small hill generally covered in scrub, granite rocks and boulders.

Mamba

Among Africa's deadliest snakes, with venom that is neurotoxic and very potent. Front-fixed fang snakes, mambas are swift and agile, and come in two versions. The aggressive *Black mamba*, as long as 4.5m, rears up to strike (without treatment with antivenin its fatality rate is virtually 100%); the *Green mamba* is more arboreal, smaller and less aggressive.

Marula fruit

The fruit of the Marula tree, and one of the best known wild fruits of Africa. Juicy, with a sweet-acid flavour, marulas are much loved by elephants and monkeys.

Mopane worms

Gaudily coloured caterpillars of the emperor moth family, mopane worms feed primarily on the leaves of the mopane tree which grows over much of Africa. In some parts, the fully grown worms are harvested and dried as a nutritious snack. Mopane leaves are in themselves nutritious fodder for buck, retaining their food value weeks after falling.

Mud hornet

A type of large wasp, black in colouring, which builds a nest out of compacted mud where it lays its eggs. A mud hornet nest constructed on the inside of an eyepiece of a pair of binoculars can blind a person; one built inside a gun barrel can prove fatal.

Nightjar

Large-eyed, long-winged nocturnal birds of medium size, several similarly arrayed species of nightjar inhabit Africa, and except for calls specific to each, are difficult to distinguish apart in the field. Their soft bark-and-dead-leaf plumage offers ideal camouflage when resting on branches or on the ground by day. They fly silently like owls, feeding on insects caught on the wing for which their weak bills and wide gapes are well adapted.

Pug-mark

The footprint of an animal, after the **Hindi** for foot; especially the print of a wild mammal.

Raptor

Generally any bird of prey. The term raptor derives from the **Latin** "to seize and carry off", and is sometimes restricted to the diurnal birds of prey - hawks, eagles, vultures, falcons etc. In the broader sense raptor is synonymous with the designation "bird of prey", and thereby embraces the nocturnal birds of prey - the owls.

Rutting season

Otherwise known as "the rut" - the annual mating season when a recurring state of sexual excitement occurs among the sexually mature members of a natural population of mammals.

Spoor

The footprint, tracks, and trail in droppings, scents and sounds left by an animal. Spoor is interpreted as "ground" spoor by way of prints left by an animal on the ground surface, together with "aerial" spoor in sign left on or above the ground, viz droppings; sticks, stones or vegetation disturbed; broken spider webs; or traces of an animal in smells and sounds.

Tree hyrax

The mainly arboreal member species of the hyrax or dassie family: endearing mammals that resemble marmots, are the size of a large rabbit and mostly adapted to rocky habitats (hence the common name "rock rabbit"). While there's little to distinguish one dassie species from another in the field, the *Tree hyrax* is recognisable by a preference for hollow trees or dense foliage, often high up, and for eerie wails uttered after dusk that rise to a piercing scream.

Tsetse fly

Confined to Africa, there are approximately 21 species of tsetse - a name derived from the **Tswana** language, and said to suggest the buzzing of the fly. More than half transmit *sleeping sickness* to humans, and *nagana* to domestic animals. The tsetse feeds on blood, and there are currently no effective controls beyond environmental ones.

Vibrissae

The bristly hairs on an animal's face - notably the whiskers of a cat. Heaviest around the upper lips, with some on each cheek, chin, and above the eyes, vibrissae are important tactile organs that supply information about immediate surroundings. As the slightest movement stimulates nerve endings, vibrissae may detect deflected air currents, and with special muscles to move them, can even be put on alert.

Viscera

The soft contents of the principal cavities of the body, viz the internal organs, especially the heart, liver, kidneys etc., together with the intestines.

Water skimmer

A fast-flying bird that frequents lakes and rivers. With wings so long they project way beyond the skimmer's forked tail when at rest, this tern-like bird skims so low over the water when feeding, it literally ploughs the surface with its projecting, and very distinctive blade-like lower mandible.